How to Resolve 7 DEADLY STRESSES

and Discover Five Causes of All Diseases

Powerful truths that transcend all cultures, nationalities, religions, and political systems!

Institute in Basic Life Principles
Box One • Oak Brook, Illinois

Published by the Institute in Basic Life Principles, Inc.

080260, Second Printing 6/08, First Edition Rev. 6/08

All Scripture verses are quoted from the King James Version of the Bible unless otherwise noted. All emphasis added.

Special thanks to our editorial, graphic arts, and printing departments for the outstanding work they have done on this book.

Special thanks to C. Stephen Paine Jr., M.D., for many long, tireless hours of research, review, and documentation in the production of this book.

Box One
Oak Brook, IL 60522-3001
Tel: 630-323-9800, Fax: 630-323-7271
www.iblp.org

Contents

1

What Is Total Health?

Total health is not merely the absence of mental, emotional, or physical sickness or disease. It is the dynamic and harmonious interaction of spirit, soul, and body.

Thus Paul prayed, "The very God of *peace* sanctify[1] you wholly; and I pray God your whole spirit and soul and body be preserved blameless unto the coming of our Lord Jesus Christ. Faithful is he that calleth you, who also will do it."[2]

The "Real You"

Total health begins with a realization that you are made up of three distinct parts: spirit, soul, and body. The most important of these is your spirit.

This is a vital point, because you will never understand or achieve total health without a working knowledge of the interaction of your spirit, soul, and body.

When God created Adam, He said, "Let us make man in our image, after our likeness."[3] The word *image* refers to God's spiritual nature, because "God is a Spirit: and they that worship him must worship him in spirit and in truth."[4]

Your spirit is able to communicate with God's Spirit and the spirits of other people. With your spirit, you are also able to discern realities that are not easily understood with the intellect of your soul.

Paul explains this by saying, "The natural man receiveth not the things of the Spirit of God: for they are foolishness unto him: neither can he know them, because they are spiritually discerned."[5]

Not only is God a Spirit, but the Godhead is a Trinity, and He has made us in His likeness. There are many Biblical confirmations that we are made in three parts.

One significant evidence is that there are three different laws that operate within us. There is the law of the spirit, the law of the mind (soul), and the law of sin in the body.[6]

When these three laws are in conflict with one another, we will experience stress, disease, and premature death. When they are in harmony with one another, we will experience health, peace, and life. "For to be carnally minded is death; but to be spiritually minded is life and peace."[7]

The Origin of Sickness and Death

This three-part nature of the human being explains what happened in the Garden of Eden. God told Adam that the very day that he ate the forbidden fruit, he would die. But Satan said to Eve, "Ye shall not surely die."[8] Adam

The peace of God is a state of undisturbed well-being with an absence of all inward strife and stress.

The Greek word for *peace* is *ēirēne*, which indicates rest in contrast to strife.[9] This comes by learning about Jesus, Who promises, "Learn of me . . . and ye shall find rest unto your souls."[10] Jesus makes Himself known to us through the forty-nine commands that He gave.[11]

To be sanctified is to withdraw your spirit, soul, and body from the unhealthy entanglements of our corrupt culture and experience true fellowship with the God of peace.

Courtesy of www.SolveFamilyProblems.com

Your body is the temple of God. Like Solomon's Temple, it has three distinct parts.

The first part of the Temple was the altar upon which sacrifices were made. The second part, the holy place, contained the showbread, the oil lamps, and the bowl of incense. The third part, the holy of holies, contained the Ark of the covenant.

The daily functions of replacing the showbread, trimming the lamps, and filling the bowl of incense are now to be carried out in our bodies. We are to present our bodies as living sacrifices. We are to feed daily on God's Word, ask our Father to fill our souls with His Holy Spirit, and pray without ceasing. Then we are to have intimate fellowship with God in our spirits.

Throughout God's universe, we see His three-part design pattern, like that of water, ice, and vapor.

and Eve ate the forbidden fruit yet remained "alive." So who was correct? God was!

Adam and Eve both died. They were spirits, and their spirits died—only their bodies and souls continued to live. Not only did Adam and Eve die that day, but all their descendants have been born spiritually dead.[12]

The only way for us to become alive is to be born again by the Spirit of God. Jesus made this clear to a religious ruler named Nicodemus.

"Verily, verily, I say unto thee . . . . Ye must be born again."[13] Nicodemus did not understand this truth and asked, "How can a man be born when he is old? can he enter the second time into his mother's womb, and be born?"[14]

The Goal of Total Health

Total health is not perfect health. Perfect health is not possible, because we all are in the process of dying physically. Paul points this out when he states, "Though our outward man perish, yet the inward man is renewed day by day."[15]

Total health is the ability to fulfill the purposes for which God created you. Every single one of us is loved by God and very precious to Him. Before you were even born, God designed you in His heart to carry out great works.[16]

Your identity and fulfillment in life is to carry out these great works. It is for this reason that you do not want any sickness or disease, which would hinder you from carrying out your life purpose.

Total health is based on realizing that you have a limited number of days in which to accomplish the great works for which God brought you into this world. Therefore, your attention must not be focused on having better health but on completing your life purpose.

Designed Before Conception

Before you were ever formed in your mother's womb, you were designed in the heart of God. This is the message that God declared to Jeremiah when He said, "Before I formed thee in the belly I knew thee; and before thou camest forth out of the womb I sanctified thee, and I ordained thee a prophet unto the nations."[17]

This is the same commission that Jesus gives to every believer today: "Go ye therefore, and teach all nations . . . to observe all things whatsoever I have commanded you."[18]

This would include the forty-nine commands that Jesus gave His disciples, which we are to learn and do in order to be His disciples also. They are based on the two great commandments—love God and love one another.

God promised His people that if they would love Him and keep His commandments, He would bless them more than all other peoples of the earth: "Keep therefore and do them [God's commandments]; for this is your wisdom and your understanding in the sight of the nations, which shall hear all these statutes, and say, Surely this great nation is a wise and understanding people. . . . And the LORD will take away from thee all sickness."[19]

Total Health: Being "Made Whole"

Total health was demonstrated by Jesus when He healed the ten lepers.[20] Leprosy was a dreaded disease in His day because of the putrid and infectious sores it caused.

1. Cleansing the Blood

The initial step of healing was not just to renew the skin but to cleanse the blood from the impurities that manifested themselves in the disease. Thus Scripture states that "as they went, they were cleansed [vs. healed]."

The Greek word translated *cleansed* is *katharízō,* which means "to purify." In a physical sense, this would refer primarily to the circulatory system, because "the life of the flesh is in the blood."[21] In a spiritual sense, *katharízō* refers to the removal of the pollution and guilt of sin.[22]

2. Healing the Flesh

The next phrase in this account tells us that they saw that they were healed. The Greek word used for *healed* is *iáomai,* which means "to restore to bodily health."[23] This would indicate that the physical symptoms of the disease had disappeared. Once the blood is cleansed from its impurities, the flesh is able to be restored to health.

3. Achieving Wholeness

In spite of this progress toward healing, there was still a third phase to undergo. Without this third phase, there would not be total health but simply removal of the distressing condition of the disease.

Total health involves a restored relationship with God and the accompanying signs of joy, freedom, and inward peace. When one of the lepers saw that he had been healed, he returned to Jesus and "fell down on his face at his feet, giving him thanks."

Jesus said: "Were there not ten cleansed? but where are the nine? There are none found that returned to give glory to God, save this stranger." Jesus then said to him, "Arise, go thy way: thy faith hath made thee whole."

Three Aspects of Salvation

In this account, the Greek word translated *made whole* is *sozo.* In other passages, it is translated *save.* There actually are three aspects of salvation, or wholeness.

1. Salvation of the Spirit

First is the eternal salvation of the spirit. This is explained in Romans 10:9–13: "If thou shalt confess with thy mouth the Lord Jesus, and shalt believe in thine heart that God hath raised him from the dead, thou shalt be saved [*sozo*]. . . . For whosoever shall call upon the name of the Lord shall be saved [*sozo*]."

2. Salvation of the Soul

Second is the salvation of the soul. Whereas the salvation of the spirit is instantaneous and eternal, the salvation of the soul (mind, will, and emotions) is a continual process. It is accomplished by engrafting God's word into your soul and thereby building a Biblical belief system

"The mind that created the universe wrote the Bible."

—Dr. Bob Wood

The Sombrero Galaxy, pictured above, has a mass equivalent to 800 billion suns. It is fifty thousand light years across, yet it is not even visible to the naked eye.[24]

Just as there are laws that govern the universe, so there are laws that govern our health. To violate them is to invite disease and death.

God demonstrates justice by visiting the iniquities of fathers on their descendents but shows love by giving mercy to all who love Him and keep His commands.

The greatest heritage a father could pass on to his children is a strong constitution of total health.

The health of this baby will partly be determined by the lifestyle of the parents.

in your heart. Thus we a[illegible] "Receive with meekness t[illegible] grafted word, which is a[illegible] save [*sozo*] your souls."[25]

The wholeness of the so[illegible] a direct effect on physical [illegible] John said, "I wish above all [illegible] that thou mayest prosper a[illegible] in health, even as thy soul [illegible]pereth."[26]

3. Salvation of the Body

The third aspect involv[illegible] "wholeness" of the physical body, which is contingent on obedience to God's moral standards: "He that soweth to his flesh shall of the flesh reap corruption."[27]

When a member of the church at Corinth committed gross immorality, Paul commanded "to deliver such a one unto Satan for the destruction of the flesh, that the spirit may be saved in the day of the Lord Jesus."[28]

Three Primary Factors That Contribute to Health

To understand and achieve total health, you need to be aware of the following three factors.

1. Genetic Tendencies

We all inherit tendencies toward certain diseases based on weaknesses in our genetic makeup. They do not have to become diseases if we follow God's way of life.

2. Physical Constitution

A grandfather who did everything wrong lived to be ninety-eight years old. However, his two-year-old grandson is dying [illegible] s [illegible]ng [illegible] his

[illegible] 1940s, [illegible] Pottenger [illegible]ed a study [illegible] which he sep[illegible]ated cats into [illegible] five groups. The first group was fed nutritious food and remained healthy throughout their lives. The other four groups were fed "junk food."

In the first generation, the poorly fed cats developed diseases late in life. In the second generation, they developed the same diseases in the middle of their life spans, and the third generation developed them early in life.[29]

Dr. Pottenger found that his third-generation cats did not even live long enough to reproduce. When he nursed the second-generation cats to health, they could reproduce and pass on stronger and stronger genes to their offspring.

3. Various Stresses

Whether or not our genetic tendencies and weak constitutions will result in diseases will be primarily determined by the stresses in our lives according to what we think, say, and do.

There can be many causes of stress, such as trying to fulfill our responsibilities with limited time or to pay bills with inadequate finances. However, the greatest stresses come from the attitudes of anger, guilt, lust, bitterness, greed, fear, and envy. These destroy the immune system.

2

Is Total Health Total Healing?

Total healing is not possible on this earth, because the sentence of death has been placed on the physical body of every person, and we are in the process of dying. Total health refers to fulfilling the number of years for which God designed us to serve Him and the quality of life we need to carry out the work He has created us to accomplish.

Three types of illnesses are given in Scripture. When you develop an illness, you should discern which of these types you are experiencing. Based on the type of sickness, you should then carry out the appropriate Biblical responses.

1. Sickness Unto Death

As a believer in the Lord, you are indestructible until your work on earth is done. Once it has been completed, there is no point in staying around here. Heaven is a far more glorious place in which to be. Paul understood this when he said, "For I am in a strait between two, having a desire to depart, and to be with Christ; which is far better."[1]

Here, Paul is discerning the time of his departure based on the ministry that he was commissioned to carry out. Believers today should do the same. If a person has what doctors describe as a terminal illness but he believes that his work is not yet done, he can appeal to God for healing—not to just extend his life but to accomplish the work that God has called him to do.

On this basis, the psalmist prayed: "O God, thou hast taught me from my youth: and hitherto have I declared thy wondrous works. Now also when I am old and gray-headed, O God, forsake me not; until I have showed thy strength unto this generation, and thy power to every one that is to come."[2]

In order to have this outlook on life and death, we must be good stewards of the time that God has entrusted to us. We should be continually looking for better ways to redeem every hour by keeping it from going to waste and choosing the most profitable activities to advance God's kingdom. We are to "number our days, that we may apply our hearts unto wisdom."[3] If you were told today that you have a terminal disease, what reason would you give God for keeping you alive?

2. Sickness Unto Chastisement

There are physical, mental, emotional, and spiritual consequences for violating God's laws. The most severe come to

All who were healed by Jesus died. But all who believed in Jesus are still living.

"I am the resurrection, and the life: he that believeth in me, though he were dead, yet shall he live."[4]

We are indestructible until our work is done!

God chastens us through financial loss, natural disasters, physical diseases, and death.

"The LORD will smite thee with the boils of Egypt, and with the emerods, and with the scab, and with the itch, whereof thou canst not be healed. . . . Moreover he will bring upon thee all the diseases of Egypt, which thou wast afraid of; and they shall cleave unto thee. Also every sickness, and every plague . . . them will the LORD bring upon thee, until thou be destroyed."[12]

Satan's daily agenda is to look for believers whom he can disable and devour with physical diseases.

"Be sober, be vigilant; because your adversary the devil, as a roaring lion, walketh about, seeking whom he may devour: Whom resist steadfast in the faith."[13]

those who choose to violate His moral laws. "For he that soweth to his flesh shall of the flesh reap corruption."[5]

The Bible specifically mentions health consequences for dishonoring parents. "Honor thy father and thy mother, as the LORD thy God hath commanded thee; that thy days may be prolonged, and that it may go well with thee."[6] "The eye that mocketh at his father, and despiseth to obey his mother, the ravens of the valley shall pick it out, and the young eagles shall eat it."[7]

There are additional health consequences for unwise diets, especially in animal products that are high in fat, which contain toxins. God has much to say about what people should or should not eat. Peter makes reference to this when he quotes from God's dietary law.[8]

If you violate any of God's commands, you will be subject to health consequences. In His mercy, God has established the communion table as a place for thorough self-examination. This self-examination is to be carried out with utmost care.

To those who observed communion carelessly, God said, "For this cause many are weak and sickly among you, and many sleep [have died prematurely]."[9]

Therefore, if you are sick, you should ask yourself, Is this God's way of chastening me for not following His way of life?

3. Sickness Unto the Glory of God

The third type of sickness includes infirmities that God designed to bring glory to Himself. There are two ways that He can do this.

The first way is through God's supernatural healing. This was experienced by the man who was born blind.

Jesus' disciples asked Him, "Who did sin, this man, or his parents, that he was born blind? Jesus answered, Neither hath this man sinned, nor his parents: but that the works of God should be made manifest in him."[10]

Notice that Jesus designed the infirmity in this man so that years later, He could demonstrate to the crowd that He was truly the Son of God. Based on this, we must be careful not to think that just because someone has a sickness or disease, it must be due to sin on his part or his parents' part.

A second way is demonstrated by Paul. He had a physical infirmity, which he referred to as his "thorn in the flesh." Three times he appealed to God to remove it.

However, God told him, "My grace is sufficient for thee: for my strength is made perfect in weakness." Paul responded by declaring, "Most gladly therefore will I rather glory in my infirmities, that the power of Christ may rest upon me."[11]

This is an important principle, because God has given us weaknesses to prevent us from depending on our own strength or ability rather than the supernatural work of His power.

3

What Five Factors Determine Total Health?

All sickness and disease can be associated with one or more of the following five factors.[1] When proper care is given regarding these factors, you have the optimal potential to avoid or clear up the related diseases. The first three factors are the most important. Unfortunately, these are largely overlooked in modern medicine.

1. What We Think

Intellectual thoughts travel through the limbic system of the brain, directly affecting many bodily functions. Researchers have found a connection between the limbic system and the emotional memory, which includes positive thoughts such as love, joy, and peace; and negative thoughts such as anger, guilt, lust, bitterness, greed, fear, and envy.[2]

All emotional memories are stored and can be consciously or subconsciously stimulated by the senses. The brain, the heart, and the intestinal tract release neurotransmitters that result in physiological changes.[3,4,5,6] The "thoughts" of the heart prompt the greatest changes in the body, as is stated in Scripture: "For as he thinketh in his heart, so is he."[7]

2. What We Say

God states, "Death and life are in the power of the tongue."[8] This statement is far more meaningful than most people realize. Positive words produce energy for health and peace, whereas negative words result in confusion and disease.

Positive words can be expressed in praise, verbal blessings, audible prayers, and cries to God. Also, the words of God are alive and powerful.[9] We are instructed: "Keep them in the midst of thine heart. For they are life unto those that find them, and health to all their flesh. Keep thy heart with all diligence; for out of it are the issues of life."[10]

Negative words are expressed by such things as curses, ridicule, mocking, gossip, and false accusations. God compares such words to poison, fire, venom, and arrows because of the effect that they have on the physical body.[11]

They must be neutralized quickly with verbal blessings, or they will do great damage to our health. Thus we are told, "Bless them which persecute you: bless, and curse not."[12]

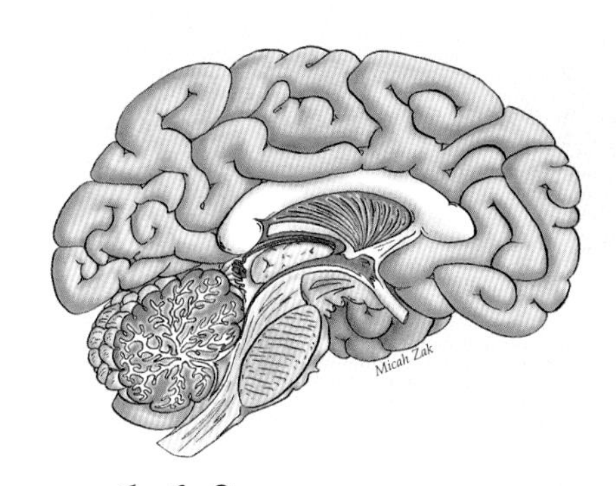

We assume that the brain does all our thinking. However, neurotransmitters are released from three different places in the body.

1. The heart
2. The brain
3. The intestines

"The word of God is . . . a discerner of the thoughts and intents of the heart."[13]

"My reins also instruct me in the night seasons."[14]

Hateful words are like the venom of a snake.

Venom, which can cause pain, nausea, swelling, and even death, can be neutralized by a positive electrical charge. Similarly, poisonous words can be overcome by a verbal blessing.

"Death and life are in the power of the tongue: and they that love it shall eat the fruit thereof."[15]

The laws of the harvest apply to what we think and do in our hearts.

- **We reap what we sow.**
- **We reap where we sow.**
- **We reap more than we sow.**
- **We reap in a different season than we sow.**

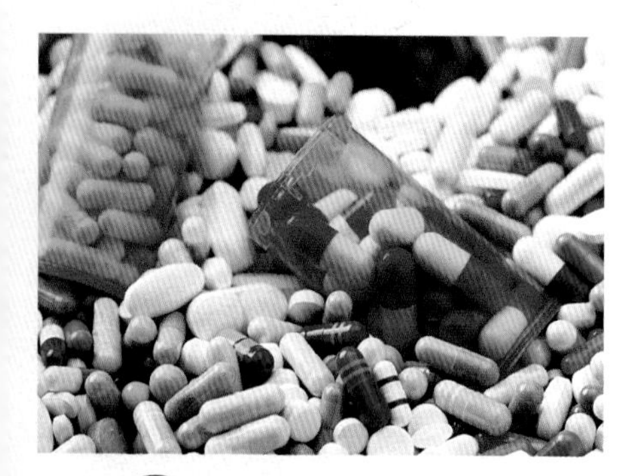

Simply taking a drug to treat a symptom is saying, "It does not matter what you think, say, do, eat, or inherit; just take this pill, and you will feel better." The result is often a side effect that requires another drug.

3. What We Do

God designed man to function in intricate cause-and-effect sequences. He prescribed a way of life that is consistent with His holy standards. If these standards are violated by our lifestyle or behavior, we will experience corresponding consequences in our health and length of life.

God compares these sequences to the laws of the harvest: "Be not deceived; God is not mocked: for whatsoever a man soweth, that shall he also reap. For he that soweth to his flesh shall of the flesh reap corruption; but he that soweth to the Spirit shall of the Spirit reap life everlasting."[16]

For example, a lifestyle of promiscuity destroys the immune system and introduces destructive viruses to the body that result in fatal diseases.

4. What We Eat

Eating nutritious food, drinking plenty of pure water, getting proper exercise, inhaling clean air, and absorbing sunshine all are important, because every cell in the body needs to be supplied with the nutrients necessary to maintain each cellular function.

However, Jesus made it clear that "Man shall not live by bread alone, but by every word that proceedeth out of the mouth of God."[17]

The first three factors of total health will have more of an effect on your physical health than what you eat, because your ability to digest food and assimilate its nutritional value is determined by what you think, say, and do.

5. What We Inherit

This factor affects all of us, because every person inherited a genetic predisposition to death through Adam's transgression. "By one man sin entered into the world, and death by sin; and so death passed upon all men, for that all have sinned."[18]

Every one of us has genetic tendencies toward certain diseases. We also have in our bodies opportunistic agents that are ready and able to spring into action just as soon as our immune systems are too weak to stop them. These disease factors include:

- **Bacteria**
- **Viruses**
- **Parasites**
- **Fungi**

The Disease Crisis of Modern Medicine

There is a place for pharmaceutical prescriptions. However, most drugs are toxic and, when taken, have what we call a side effect. A side effect is simply a toxic overload. If you simply cover a symptom with a drug and fail to identify and deal with its root causes, you are putting yourself on a course of increasing drugs and diseases.

When the stresses of anger, guilt, lust, bitterness, greed, fear, and envy are resolved by obeying the commands of Christ, the sickness or disease they caused often clears up.

Scripture promises that when we follow God's ways, our "health shall spring forth speedily."[19]

Does the Heart Think?

Until recently, people considered the heart to be simply a muscle that pumps blood to the rest of the body. However, the One Who designed the heart ascribes to it the capacity to think and reason,[1] feel emotion,[2] and make decisions.[3]

In recent years, there has been a renewed interest in studying the capability of the heart to function as an intelligence center.[4,5,6] What researchers have found is both amazing and vital to our ability to achieve total health. When we understand this aspect of our lives, we will realize why God warns us to guard the heart "with all diligence; for out of it are the issues of life."[7]

The Marvels of the Heart

The endurance and efficiency of a healthy, average heart are amazing! The heart beats 100,000 times a day, pumping 2,000 gallons of blood through 60,000 miles of veins, arteries, and capillaries. During an average lifetime, the human heart will beat more than 2.5 billion times! It will pump about 1 million barrels of blood—enough to fill more than three supertankers![8]

The body contains only about 6 quarts of blood, which circulates through the cardiovascular system three times every minute.

The Brain of the Heart

Researchers were baffled when they discovered that the heart begins its incredible functions before the brain is developed in the womb. Recent discoveries have revealed that the heart contains cells that make and release a large number of neurotransmitters, which were previously thought to be produced only in the brain.

This discovery further affirms that the heart has its own "brain," which communicates with the brain in the head through the nervous system, hormonal system, and other pathways.[9,10,11]

The Electrical System

The heart produces an electrical field that is sixty times stronger than the field produced by the brain, and the magnetic field of the heart is five thousand times stronger than the field generated by the brain.[12]

The normal frequency range of the electrical activity in the brain is between 0 and 100 Hz, whereas the normal frequency of the heart is 250 Hz. Input from

The human heart pumps enough blood during its lifetime to fill more than three supertankers! But that is just the beginning of its marvelous wonders.

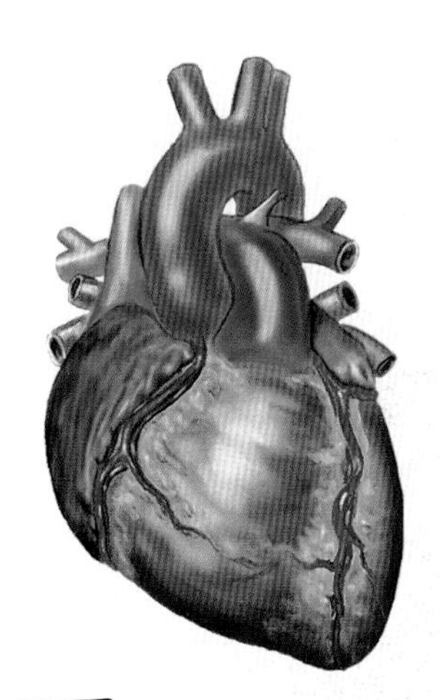

It is by the belief system of the heart that we think, speak, and act. This is a vital principle of total health.

You will never control the words of your mouth with your brain, because "out of the abundance of the heart the mouth speaketh."[13]

"Those things which proceed out of the mouth come forth from the heart; and they defile the man. For out of the heart proceed evil thoughts, murders, adulteries, fornications, thefts, false witness, blasphemies."[14]

The electromagnetic field of the heart is like a huge radio tower that sends out signals to the world.

The low frequency of the heart is similar to the sonar frequency used in submarines in that it can transmit unhindered to faraway locations.

Music bypasses the brain and becomes a part of the heart's belief system.

the heart to the brain can either inhibit or facilitate the activity of the brain. In his book *Everyday Miracles by God's Design,* Dr. David Jernigan writes: "Within this context the heart is considered a single entity. The 'brain in the heart' is a network of neurons, neurotransmitters, and proteins that send messages between neurons."[15]

Like the brain, the heart has support cells and a complex circuitry that enables it to act independently, learn, remember, and produce the "feeling of the heart."[16]

The type of information sent from the heart to the brain has a profound effect on higher functions, influencing perceptions, emotions, and thought processes.[17,18,19] The heart is the primary means by which a person seeks and perceives God.

God points out, "Ye shall seek me, and find me, when ye shall search for me with all your heart."[20] The psalmist testified, "With my whole heart have I sought thee: O let me not wander from thy commandments."[21] In order to control our thoughts, we must go beyond the "battle for the mind" and engage in a "battle for the heart."

How Stress Affects the Heart

When a thought enters your mind, you have an immediate responsibility to filter it through God's wisdom and reject it if it does not acknowledge the way, truth, and life of Christ. Paul explains: "The weapons of our warfare are . . . mighty . . . Casting down imaginations, and every high thing that exalteth itself against the knowledge of God, and bringing into captivity every thought to the obedience of Christ."[22]

If stressful thoughts are allowed to go from your mind to your heart, they will become a part of your belief system and impair your body's resistance, allowing sickness and disease. It is certainly true that as a person "thinketh in his heart, so is he."[23]

A New Look at "Amusement"

The type of entertainment that you allow yourself to enjoy will have a profound effect on the belief system of your heart and, thus, the words of your mouth, the decisions you make, and the actions you carry out in your life.

The word *amuse* is made up of two words from the Old French: *A* means "to," and *muser* means "to divert." It implies diverting attention from what is serious or important. To be amused is to bypass your mind and not to think about what is going directly to your heart's belief system.

The type of music you listen to is especially important, because music is the most powerful form of worship. For this reason, the command to be filled with God's Spirit is followed by instructions to sing and make melody in our hearts to the Lord.[24]

There are two powerful messages that come from music. The first and most powerful is the message of the music. The second and less powerful is the message of the lyrics.

The tremendous effect of melodious music on the health of a person is seen in King Saul's deliverance from overpowering rage by David. When David played melodious music on his harp, the evil spirits could not stand to listen to it, and they left.[25]

5

Factor 1: What We Think

The thoughts of your intellect are ideas that can change with new information. However, the thoughts of your heart make up your belief system and dictate what you think, say, and do.[1]

If you have ever tried to control every word you say, you have no doubt experienced how impossible that is. Scripture explains the problem: "The tongue can no man tame; it is an unruly evil, full of deadly poison."[2]

Why is the tongue so untamable? The tongue is not controlled by the intellect, will power, or emotions. It is controlled by the belief system of the heart: "For out of the abundance of the heart the mouth speaketh."[3] Therefore, if you want to control your tongue, you must first change the belief system of your heart.

Similarly, you may know in your intellect that certain behavior is wrong, hate the deeds of that behavior with your emotions, and purpose with your will that you will no longer behave in such a way. All of this is to no avail, because the belief system of your heart will control your actions.[4]

Thus Paul writes: "For what I would [do], that do I not; but what I hate, that do I. . . . O wretched man that I am! who shall deliver me from the body of this death?"[5]

The Heart and Health

The belief system of the heart controls the release of neurotransmitters and hormones that determine health. For example, studies have shown that people who have faith have stronger immune systems and better health than those who do not.[6]

Faith comes by the Word of God, which should make up the belief system of the heart. Every system in the body is directly affected by the thoughts of the heart. Joyful thoughts will strengthen the immune system[7] as Scripture states: "A merry heart doeth good like a medicine: but a broken spirit drieth the bones."[8]

A clear demonstration of the influence that thoughts have on health is seen in the results of patients who take placebos. A placebo is used to measure the effectiveness of a proposed drug. While certain patients are given the actual drug, others are given something that looks like the drug but contains nothing of substance.

A surprising number of test subjects who take a placebo

Each planet has a frequency that is in harmony with every other planet.[9]

If our music is not in harmony with God's universe, we will lack inward peace and suffer in our health.

The attraction and addiction of loud, dissonant sound is that it causes a continuous adrenaline rush. This activates other hormonal impulses and disorders.

The average American's life expectancy is 77 years. More than three hundred top rock stars had an average life span of 37 years, while orchestra conductors have a life expectancy of 89 years.[10,11]

Faith is a key factor in healing. But faith must be based on Scripture. On the Mount of Olives, Jesus spoke of faith moving "this mountain." This teaching was based on Zechariah's prophecy that one day this will happen.[21]

Courtesy of www.SolveFamilyProblems.com

It would have been more profitable for Samson to have lost one eye than to have had both eyes gouged out, lost his freedom, and been forced to labor in a cold prison, serving his enemies amid the taunt and ridicule of curious onlookers.

actually get better, because they believe in their hearts that it will work.[12] In some studies, the number of patients who were helped by the placebo was the same as the number of those helped by the drug—and the placebo had no damaging side effects![13,14]

Jesus points out the connection between the beliefs of the heart and faith that can accomplish miraculous works: "Verily I say unto you, That whosoever shall say unto this mountain, Be thou removed, and be thou cast into the sea; and shall not doubt in his heart, but shall believe that those things which he saith shall come to pass; he shall have whatsoever he saith."[15]

The Power of Thoughts for Life or Death

There is a reason why the Bible warns us to guard our hearts with all diligence. The issues of life and death that come out of it affect not only us but also everyone around us.

Jesus applied this principle to lust. He said, "Whosoever looketh on a woman to lust after her hath committed adultery with her already in his heart."[16]

Notice that Jesus does not just say that the lustful man commits adultery in his heart but rather that he commits adultery *with her.* His lust has a destructive effect on her heart as well as his own.

The effect that the thoughts of our hearts have on other people can be understood by the fact that someone can often sense when a person behind him is staring at him. He cannot see or hear the person. But the frequency and magnetic field of the person's heart directly affects the frequency and magnetic field of his heart in a negative or a positive way.

Often girls are plagued by immoral thoughts and wonder what is causing them. It rarely occurs to them that their immodest dress will cause men to lust after them in their hearts.

Scripture challenges young men to be strong in this area: "Why wilt thou, my son, be ravished with a strange woman, and embrace the bosom of a stranger? For the ways of man are before the eyes of the LORD, and he pondereth all his going.

"His own iniquities shall take the wicked himself, and he shall be holden with the cords of his sins. He shall die without instruction; and in the greatness of his folly he shall go astray."[17]

No wonder Jesus counsels that it would be better to lose a right eye or hand than to have our whole bodies cast on the rubbish heap with disease and death.[18]

The beliefs of the heart can lead to either health or destruction: "For out of the heart proceed evil thoughts, murders, adulteries, fornications, thefts, false witness, blasphemies: These are the things which defile a man."[19]

The evil thoughts that produce the corruptions of sickness, disease, and premature death stem from seven destructive stresses.

These stresses are given by Jesus in the Sermon on the Mount. They are anger, guilt, lust, bitterness, greed, fear, and envy. Each of these stresses directly affects the systems of the body, determining health or sickness.[20]

6

Factor 2: What We Say

One of the most inaccurate rhymes of all time is "sticks and stones may break my bones, but words will never hurt me." Words can be so hurtful and damaging to a person's health that God compares them to deadly poison, fire, and sharp arrows.[1]

Furthermore, "The words of a talebearer are as *wounds*, and they go down into the innermost parts of the belly."[2]

When someone curses you, especially a parent, his words lodge deep into your soul. If you become bitter, the words spread like a poison that affects your whole body. The longer these words stay within you, the greater the damage they will do to your spirit, soul, and body.

The Power of Verbal Blessings

Just as destructive words can spread death, so encouraging words can spread life. God states, "A good report maketh the bones fat [healthy]."[3]

One of the most powerful ways to improve your health and the health of those around you is to learn the skill of giving verbal blessings. In order to give such a blessing, you must first identify qualities that are missing in another person, then ask God to bless that person with the development of these qualities.

For example, if one of your family members has the stress of anger because of irritations in the home, the qualities that he needs to develop may include patience, self-control, kindness, and genuine love.

A blessing should then be spoken aloud for that person: "O God, bless [name of person] with [self-control, kindness, patience, genuine love, etc.]."

As soon as you speak this blessing, God will give that person the enabling power to develop these qualities, and He will also free you from the emotional damage of his anger. There are three important factors behind the power of a verbal blessing.

1. Invoke God's Name

The name of God is powerful. When you use it to bless a person, God gives that person the desire and power to carry out the blessing. This enabling power is described when God said, "And they shall put my name upon the children of Israel; and I will bless them."[4]

In the fires of hell, one member of the body will suffer more than any other!

An eyewitness reveals what member that is. In hell, the rich man cried out, "Father Abraham, have mercy on me, and send Lazarus, that he may dip the tip of his finger in water, and cool my tongue; for I am tormented in this flame."[5]

The power of words to give more abundant life to people may also enrich our food, based on Paul's instruction to receive food with thanksgiving.

Meats that have been provided by God for our consumption are "sanctified by the word of God and prayer."[6]

The power of words to affect even plant life was illustrated in an experiment.

Cooked white rice was put into the two jars pictured above.

The jars were placed on a shelf in a quiet room 3 to 4 feet apart. Each day the rice on the left was given verbal blessings, and the rice on the right was given verbal curses.

After seventeen days, the rice in the left jar remained white, whereas the rice in the right jar turned dark. When the lids were opened, a sweet aroma came from the left jar, but a putrid stench came from the right jar.

If this happened to cooked rice, imagine what happens to the internal terrain of people who receive blessings or curses!

A family in New Zealand demonstrated this principle. Nothing they did would motivate their seven-year-old son, Samuel, to overcome his continual sadness until his mother asked God to bless him with a radiant countenance, joy in his heart, and a smile that would administer life to others. Even as she spoke, a smile broke out on his face and he became a joy giver in the family.

2. Speak Aloud

There is power in the spoken word; it can be used for good or for evil. "Death and life are in the power of the tongue: and they that love it shall eat the fruit thereof."[7]

No wonder God holds us accountable for every idle word we speak. "I say unto you, That every idle word that men shall speak, they shall give account thereof in the day of judgment."[8]

3. Use Biblical Truth

The Word of God is living and powerful. When you use it in a blessing, it will further enable the person you bless to develop the qualities he needs. "For the word of God is quick, and powerful, and sharper than any two-edged sword."[9]

How Verbal Blessings Bring Healing

When people lash out with bitter words, it is as if you have been bitten by a poisonous snake. The venom of their words penetrates your mental and emotional systems and continues to damage your health until the hurts are resolved.

God describes the nature of these verbal curses by comparing the tongue to deadly poison. "But the tongue can no man tame; it is an unruly evil, full of deadly poison."[10] It is also compared to a raging fire that will continue to burn within you and turn into bitterness and hate: "The tongue is a fire, a world of iniquity: so is the tongue among our members, that it defileth the whole body, and setteth on fire the course of nature; and it is set on fire of hell."[11]

When a person is bitten by a poisonous snake, the toxic venom enters his bloodstream, causing swelling, pain, nausea, toxic shock, and possible death.[12]

However, this deadly poison can be removed by neutralizing the venom of the snake bite, usually by using antivenin. Another treatment that may be effective is to apply an electrical impulse to the bite. This positive charge can neutralize the negatively charged venom. This principle applies when you give a verbal blessing to those who curse you. Thus God commands, "Bless them which persecute you: bless, and curse not."[13]

There is a special reward for those who return blessing for cursing: "Not rendering evil for evil, or railing for railing: but contrariwise blessing; knowing that ye are thereunto called, that ye should inherit a blessing."[14]

What We Say to Ourselves

The most important conversations that you have every day are those that take place between your spirit and your soul. Your soul may say such things as "I'm worthless," "I don't like myself," "I will never amount to anything," "I cannot succeed," "I'm unable to break this addiction," "I'm too weak to do any work," "I'm going to die in a few years," etc.

These are curses that you can put upon yourself. They are self-fulfilling prophesies that will do great damage to your mental, emotional, physical, and spiritual health unless you neutralize each thought with Scriptural truth.

Because we have the ability to speak life or death to ourselves,

God has given the instruction to live in truth by "Casting down imaginations, and every high thing that exalteth itself against the knowledge of God, and bringing into captivity every thought to the obedience of Christ."[15]

David wrote: "LORD, who shall abide in thy tabernacle? who shall dwell in thy holy hill? He that walketh uprightly, and worketh righteousness, and speaketh the truth in his heart."[16]

By speaking the truth in our hearts, we will build a belief system by which we are able to overcome temptations and walk in God's ways. God's ways lead to life, peace, and health.

What We Say to God

God designed man to maintain a continual conversation with Him. For this reason, we are instructed to meditate on His Word day and night[17] and "Pray without ceasing."[18]

When this fellowship is maintained, your whole being will be in harmony with the Spirit of God. Since God is life, you will thus experience life-giving energy within your being. This is the very purpose for which Jesus came: "I am come that they might have life, and that they might have it more abundantly."[19]

When the life that God describes in His commands is carried out in our daily decisions, we will achieve a level of inward peace that generates an internal terrain, or chemistry, that is required to enjoy a state of optimal health. God promises this to those who live in the light of His Word: "It shall be health to thy navel, and marrow to thy bones."[20]

Learning God's Language

God is an infinitely wise and holy Sovereign. His thoughts and ways are as far above our thoughts and ways as the heavens are above the earth. Therefore, the only way we can carry on an intelligent conversation with Him is to learn His way of thinking. This is done by memorizing and meditating on His Word, especially the commands of Christ.

By saturating your heart and soul with God's thoughts, you will be able to use them to express your own mind, will, and emotions. You will thus be able to fulfill the quality of worship that God desires. "But the hour cometh, and now is, when the true worshipers shall worship the Father in spirit and in truth: for the Father seeketh such to worship him."[21]

This is the purpose for memorizing and meditating on Scripture. God promises success to everyone who honors His Word in this way.[22]

Using God's Language

As you continue to hide God's Word in your heart and purify your soul by obeying it, you will be able to use Scripture as a weapon to defeat Satan's temptations. Jesus did this when Satan tempted Him in the wilderness. Three times Satan presented a clever temptation, and three times Jesus responded by saying, "It is written . . . ."[23]

We can use Scriptural truths to design verbal blessings for others, and we can claim God's promises as we cry out for deliverance from the destruction of deadly diseases.

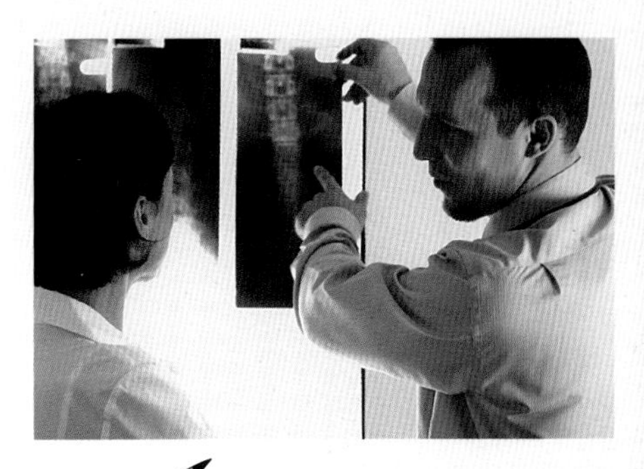

A good report (from God and others) leads to healthy bones.

"Pleasant words are as a honeycomb, sweet to the soul, and health to the bones."[24]

Sins and transgressions emit energy, and energy cannot be destroyed. It goes into space and is therefore always before the eyes of God unless He blots it out.

God identifies the continuing energy of sound by saying to Cain, "The voice of thy brother's blood crieth unto me from the ground."[25]

"According to thy lovingkindness: according unto the multitude of thy tender mercies blot out my transgressions. Wash me throughly from mine iniquity, and cleanse me from my sin."[26]

In Creation, the Spirit of God moved upon the face of the water as a *gentle breeze* and participated in the creation of man from the dust of the ground.

In the new birth, the Spirit of God manifests Himself as a *blowing wind* that indwells a person's spirit.

In the upper room, the Spirit of God came upon the group as a *mighty, rushing wind* and filled them with supernatural power.

The Spirit's Power

The Holy Spirit reveals Himself as "air in motion." The Greek word for *spirit* is *pneuma,* which means "wind."

The first reference to the Holy Spirit is in Genesis when "The Spirit of God moved upon the face of the waters."[27] The Hebrew word for *moved* is *râchaph,* which indicates a fluttering breeze.

In Jesus' conversation with Nicodemus about the new birth, He described the Spirit as a blowing wind.[28] When the Holy Spirit came upon the 120 disciples in the upper room, He manifested Himself as a "rushing mighty wind."[29]

The Power of Life and Death With "Air in Motion"

It is significant to realize that our words are a result of air in motion. When the air from our lungs passes through our vocal cords, sound is produced.

Our words can be energized by the Holy Spirit and produce life, or they can be motivated by anger, guilt, bitterness, or other stresses and bring about death. On this basis, "Death and life are in the power of the tongue."[30]

The Power of Words for Faith and Salvation

The power of faith is a function of the Holy Spirit and is manifested by the words of our mouths, which express the beliefs of our hearts. Therefore, Jesus declared, "Have faith in God. For verily I say unto you, That whosoever shall say . . . and shall not doubt in his heart, but shall believe that those things which he *saith* shall come to pass; he shall have whatsoever he *saith.*"[31]

This awesome principle of the power of God being exercised through the spoken words from the heart was a foundational message of Paul.

"The word is nigh thee, even in thy mouth, and in thy heart: that is, the word of faith, which we preach; That if thou shalt confess with thy mouth the Lord Jesus, and shalt believe in thine heart that God hath raised him from the dead, thou shalt be saved.

"For with the heart man believeth unto righteousness; and with the mouth confession is made unto salvation. . . . For whosoever shall call upon the name of the Lord shall be saved."[32]

The Power of Words to Activate Transformations

The principle of air in motion is also basic to the power of verbal blessings. When you ask God to bless others with character qualities, the Holy Spirit energizes them with the power of grace to carry out your words of blessing.

For this purpose, we are told to bless those who curse us. God promises that if we bless them, we ourselves will inherit a blessing. "Not rendering evil for evil, or railing for railing [words of death]: but contrariwise blessing; knowing that ye are thereunto called, that ye should inherit a blessing."[33]

7

Factor 3: What We Do

The Law of Cause and Effect

Just as there are physical laws that govern the universe, so there are spiritual laws that control our relationships with God and others. These laws also determine our level of health or sickness.

These spiritual laws are imprinted in the heart of every person![1] From early childhood, we instinctively know when we are about to do something right or wrong. If we discern in our spirits that it is wrong, we may be tempted to do it in secret.

Once we commit a wrongdoing, it is inscribed in the memory of the limbic system, which is like the filing system of the brain. The more we do wrong, the more guilt we carry. This guilt directly affects our relationships with God and other people.

When Adam and Eve transgressed God's command, the eyes of their consciences were opened, and they recognized their sinful condition. It was then that they were afraid and tried to hide from the presence of God.[2]

The Pain of Conscience

When we do things that we know are wrong, we instantly experience a "pain of conscience." The body does not like pain, so we will do whatever we can to remove it.

The quickest and most effective way to resolve the pain is to confess our wrongdoing to God and to those whom we have hurt. "If we confess our sins, he is faithful and just to forgive us our sins, and to cleanse us from all unrighteousness."[3]

However, our natural inclination is to act in pride by hiding our sins and transgressions. God warns, "He that covereth his sins shall not prosper: but whoso confesseth and forsaketh them shall have mercy."[4]

If we choose to cover our sins, our intellects will deal with the pain in our consciences by thinking up reasons why our sins and transgressions are not really all that bad. We will rationalize and justify what we did, or we will challenge the laws that we violated. We may even come to the mental state of questioning or denying the existence of God.

The Effect on the Bones

Hidden sin directly affects the health of the bones, and the health of the bones directly affects

To sin is to come short of standards that a holy, sinless God requires to have fellowship with Him.

"All have sinned, and come short of the glory of God."[5] "The wages of sin is death; but the gift of God is eternal life through Jesus Christ our Lord."[6]

To transgress is to go over the line that God has established in His holy Law.

"Where no law is, there is no transgression."[7]

"If . . . every transgression and disobedience received a just recompence of reward; How shall we escape, if we neglect so great salvation?"[8]

Socrates Nietzsche Plato

A man's morality will tend to dictate his philosophy and his theology.

Socrates and Plato developed philosophies contrary to God's way of life. This was because they committed in their personal lives sins and transgressions against God's Law. Nietzsche proclaimed, "God is dead." The rebellious son of a Lutheran minister, he committed immorality and ultimately lost his mind.[25]

The strength of sin is in its secrecy.

"Men loved darkness rather than light, because their deeds were evil. For every one that doeth evil hateth the light, neither cometh to the light, lest his deeds should be reproved."[26]

Satan rules the kingdom of darkness. As long as we hide our secret sins, we are under the bondage and torment of his control.

the health of the rest of the body. This is because blood cells are manufactured in the marrow of the bones.

Scripture makes a distinction between bones and flesh. When Adam saw Eve, he said, "This is now bone of my *bones,* and flesh of my *flesh:* she shall be called Woman, because she was taken out of Man [Adam's rib bone]."[9]

The effect that sin has on the bones is recorded by the psalmist: "Have mercy upon me, O LORD; for I am weak: O LORD, heal me; for my bones are vexed."[10] The Hebrew word for *vexed* means "to tremble inwardly, to palpitate, to be alarmed or agitated." The psalmist continues by associating the vexation of his bones with the vexation of his soul: "My soul is also sore vexed."[11]

The guilt of sin causes the bones to grow old and become dehydrated. Thus David wrote: "Blessed is he whose transgression is forgiven, whose sin is covered. . . . When I kept silence, my bones waxed old through my roaring all the day long."[12]

Based on the terrible price we pay for violating God's Law and failing to confess our sin, we would do well to heed the counsel of the wisest man who ever lived: "Be not wise in thine own eyes: fear the LORD, and depart from evil."[13]

Corruption of the Mind

A man's morality will tend to dictate his theology and philosophy. Thus if a person allows himself to act immorally and violate God's laws, which are written on his heart and conscience, he will soon begin to think incoherently.[14] A great deal of schizophrenia can be traced to secret moral failures that were never confessed.[15] God warns that if we reject the truth, He will send a strong delusion, and we will believe a lie.[16]

Using drugs or shock treatment to deal with mental disorders does not reach the heart of the problem. At best, these treatments allow a patient to cope with life, but they do not deliver him from the bondage of his guilt.

Corruption of the Emotions

The confusion and guilt that result from immorality will also wreak havoc on the emotions, causing a continual drain of emotional energy that will lead to deep depression.

The only way to solve this emotional problem is to confess moral failures, claim the blood of Christ for forgiveness, and turn from sin.[17]

Depression is only one of many emotional problems that result from the cascade of hormonal imbalances caused by guilt.

Corruption of the Body

Sexually transmitted diseases are rampant in America, and new strains of viruses have developed for which no cures have been found.[18,19]

These viruses are directly linked to changes in DNA structures that weaken the immune system,[20,21] and they are now shown to be associated with different forms of cancer.[22]

The treatment of cancer by chemotherapy or radiation further weakens the immune system, allowing opportunistic agents to destroy health.[23,24]

The condition of our moral lives will determine the condition of our physical health.

Factor 4: What We Eat

A person who buys a new car is given an owner's manual that details how to get the best performance from the car. God has written an even more precise "operations manual" for the care of our bodies, which actually belong to Him.

God has written a manual for the care of our bodies and provided a way to experience a healthy life. However, God's manual goes far beyond what we eat or drink, because He has ordained that "Man shall not live by bread alone but by every word of God."[1]

In this verse, the Greek word for *word* is *rhema.* A rhema is a personal instruction for us to follow. For example, when Jesus told Peter to cast the net from the other side of the boat, Peter replied, "Master, we have toiled all the night, and have taken nothing: nevertheless at thy word [*rhema*] I will let down the net."[2]

Jesus gave forty-nine direct commands on how to love Him and one another. To the degree that we understand and apply them to our lives, we will enjoy good health and a long life.

One direct example of this is the command to honor our parents, "that it may be well with thee, and thou mayest live long on the earth."[3]

If a person is bitter toward his parents, sickness and disease will result no matter how much money is spent on organic food, vitamins, essential minerals, food supplements, pure water, exercise, sunshine, essential oils, colon cleanses, or herbal teas.

For this reason, Scripture warns, "Better is a dinner of herbs where love is, than a stalled ox and hatred therewith."[4]

Jesus affirms this when He says: "Do not ye yet understand, that whatsoever entereth in at the mouth goeth into the belly, and is cast out into the draught? But those things which proceed out of the mouth come forth from the heart; and they defile the man. For out of the heart proceed evil thoughts, murders, adulteries, fornications, thefts, false witness, blasphemies."[5]

Designed for Immortality

Dr. Alexis Carrel was a noted physician at the Rockefeller Institute for Medical Research. In 1912, he conducted one of the most remarkable experiments in medical history. Sadly, the significance of what he discovered has been largely ignored in medical circles. If his findings were properly understood and applied, they would transform our whole approach to medicine.

Dr. Carrel took heart tissue from a chicken embryo and immersed it in a solution of electrolyte nutrients. The solution was changed daily, waste products

Just as we do not put pollutants into our gas tanks, so we should not put unclean meats into our bodies.

The kidneys are able to eliminate mineral salts (measured in electrical conductance) of up to 12,000 microsiemens (μS). Greater amounts will burden the body and require storage in fat. A serving of chicken produces a measurable mineral salt load equivalent to 150 μS, well-cooked beef produces 250 μS, and pork produces 12,000 μS.[6]

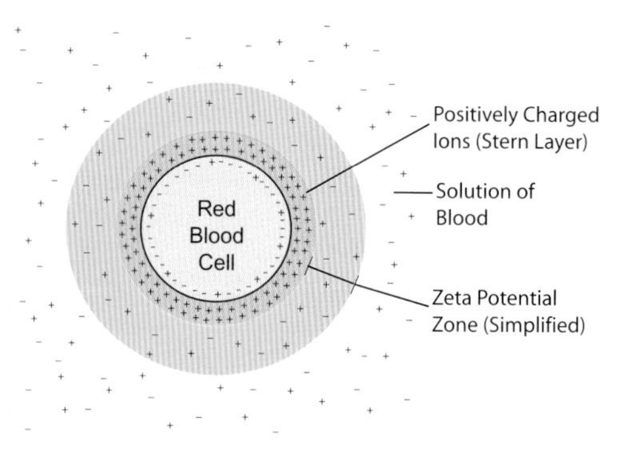

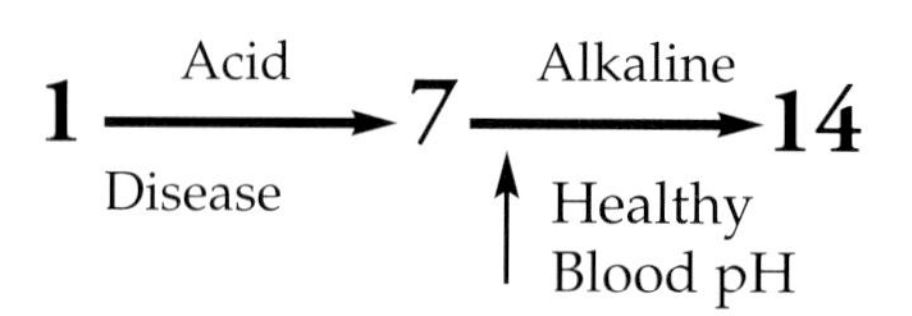

Alkaline Foods

Spinach	*4 c.*	+556
Molasses	*1 tsp.*	+360
Celery	*5 stalks*	+341
Carrots	*3*	+282
Lettuce	*1/2 head*	+170
Broccoli	*1 c.*	+101
Brussels sprouts	*6*	+95
Cucumber	*10 slices*	+71
Radishes	*7*	+64
Cauliflower	*1 c.*	+50
Pineapple	*1 c.*	+44
Raisins	*1/2 c.*	+42
Strawberries	*12*	+28
Sweet potato	*1*	+26
Lemon	*1/2 c.*	+24
Orange	*1/2 c.*	+22
Banana	*1*	+18

Acidic Foods

Scallops	*1/4 c.*	-226
Oysters	*5*	-209
Sausage	*6 links*	-160
Oatmeal	*1 c.*	-95
Corned beef	*1/4 lb.*	-80
Lobster	*1/2 lb.*	-78
Noodles	*7/8 c.*	-50
Peanut butter	*3 tbsp.*	-49
Chicken	*1/4 lb.*	-43
Salmon	*1 c.*	-26
Steak	*1/4 lb.*	-24
Turkey	*1/4 lb.*	-23
Honey	*4 tbsp.*	-4

Note: Similar lists vary.[14]

were regularly removed, and fresh minerals and life-supporting nutrients were replenished.[7]

Amazingly, the heart tissue not only survived for many years, but it remained healthy throughout the entire span of the study simply because the fluids were refreshed on a regular basis. Dr. Carrel stated: "The cell is immortal. It is merely the fluid in which it floats that degenerates. Renew this fluid at intervals, give this cell something on which to feed, and so far as we know, the pulsation of life may go on forever."[8]

Dr. Carrel demonstrated his point. The average life span of a chicken is only about seven years. These chicken cells continued to live on and on until researchers stopped refreshing the nutrients thirty-four years later—two years after Dr. Carrel's death!

This study affirmed a Biblical point: God did, in fact, design our bodies to live indefinitely before the Fall. Even after the Fall, many lived more than nine hundred years.

The presence of stress and other factors cause heart cells to weaken, become diseased, and die. Since the heart is the center of life, and since "the life of the flesh is in the blood,"[9] it is important to understand the root causes that weaken and damage the heart.

A Key to Health: Electrolyte Balance

Seventeen years after Dr. T. C. McDaniel graduated from medical school, he was obese and suffered from heart palpitations and other infirmities. His medical training had not given him the answers he needed, so he began to research the chemistry of the blood and how it functions.

Michael Faraday

He was intrigued by the work of Michael Faraday and his research in electrical charges and colloidal suspensions.[10] Then he found practical answers in the work of Thomas Riddick, who used clinical trials to confirm the benefit of balanced electrolyte solutions.[11]

He began to apply what he learned with tens of thousands of patients over a forty-year period. When they followed the protocol he prescribed, they experienced relief from conditions such as blood clots, heart arrhythmias, deep vein thrombosis, kidney stones, strokes, asthma, and hemorrhoids. Patients have also reported significant benefits in reducing high blood pressure and controlling blood sugar. Dr. McDaniel was also able to spare many patients from amputation through this approach.

He himself experienced at least four heart arrhythmias that he believes would have taken his life had he not applied his knowledge of electrolyte balance. He continued to remain healthy and practice medicine into his nineties.[12]

Dr. McDaniel explains his approach to electrolyte balance with the principle of zeta potential.[13] This is a well-established concept that—if understood and applied—can minimize the need for potentially damaging forms of treatment.

How Zeta Potential Works

The principle that Dr. Alexis Carrel used to keep the chicken embryo alive for thirty-four years and that Dr. T. C. McDaniel applied to help so many patients is explained in the diagram in the left-hand column of the previous page.

Around every red blood cell are two layers of electrolytes. One is positive, and one is negative. When these two layers are strong and properly balanced, the blood cells separate from one another and easily disperse throughout the body, carrying nutrients and oxygen to every cell.

If the electrolytes are insufficient or out of balance, this causes a condition known as erythrocyte aggregation or "blood sludge," which means the red blood cells travel through the bloodstream adhering to one another. This thickens the blood, impeding circulation, making the heart work harder, and reducing the ability of the blood to transport nutrients, including oxygen, to the body.[15] Blood clots, heart arrhythmias, deep vein thrombosis, and strokes are further possible consequences of blood sludge.

Further Factors of Electrolyte Balance

In order for blood to disperse throughout the body and carry essential nutrients to every cell, there must be an adequate supply of alkaline-producing foods (ionic). Alkaline foods such as fruits, vegetables, and nuts are rich in the minerals and nutrients that are necessary for electrolyte balance.

When the internal pH of the body is slightly alkaline, diseases are not able to survive.[16] However, when the pH becomes acidic, diseases are rampant. It is on this basis that foods must be evaluated. Animal fat and certain meats are highly acidic[17,18] and will disrupt the electrolyte balance.[19] It is possibly for this reason that God gives instruction in Scripture that certain meats are not to be eaten.[20]

God gives significant promises of health to those who follow His regulations: "And the LORD will take away from thee all sickness, and will put none of the evil diseases of Egypt, which thou knowest, upon thee."[21]

The Health Benefits of Fasting

Fasting is setting aside food for specified periods of time with or without spiritual purposes. A fast cleanses the body of toxins, strengthens the immune system, and causes the organs to be rejuvenated, which slows the aging process.[22] Fasting should include purified water.

Years ago, a study was conducted at the medical school of the University of California, Berkeley. Animals with known average life spans were placed on a two-day fast each week. The life spans of the animals in the study were doubled.[23,24]

Researchers found that one day of fasting was beneficial, two were optimal, but three days of fasting were too much. This is consistent with the beneficial practice of the Pharisee who stated that he gave tithes of all that he possessed and fasted twice a week.[25]

Scripture gives many affirmations of the health benefits of fasting. One of them is found in Isaiah 58:6, 8a: "Is not this the fast that

In a university study, animals with known life expectancies were put on various lengths of fasts. Those that fasted two days a week doubled their life spans.

"When thou fastest, anoint thine head, and wash thy face; That thou appear not unto men to fast, but unto thy Father which is in secret: and thy Father, which seeth in secret, shall reward thee openly."[26]

Dehydration is a major cause of illness. Therefore, we should be alert to the evidences of this condition.[27]

- Headaches
- Lack of skin resilience
- Dizziness
- Cramping in the arms and legs
- Physical weakness
- Dry mouth and tongue
- Decreased dark yellow urine
- Low blood pressure

I have chosen? to loose the bands of wickedness, to undo the heavy burdens, and to let the oppressed go free, and that ye break every yoke? . . . Then shall thy light break forth as the morning, and thine health shall spring forth speedily."

The Need for Pure Air and Water

Pollutants in the air you breathe and water you drink will definitely affect your health. God created man with the breath of life, and Jesus compares Himself to "living water."

In addition to the purity of your drinking water, it is important that you drink a sufficient amount. Most people do not drink enough water, nor do they recognize signs of dehydration.

Health specialists recommend that a person drink the equivalent of about half his body weight in ounces every day.[28] Water not only revitalizes the body but it also flushes out impurities.

Dehydration is the root of many diseases, especially among the elderly.[29] When disease symptoms appear and drugs are used to relieve or mask the symptoms, the body's health is further damaged because of the side effects of the drugs and the failure to correct the basic cause, which may simply be a lack of water.

Natural Treatments

For every sickness, there is probably a natural, inexpensive remedy. Unfortunately, these solutions have not been promoted, because the focus of today's medical community is on pharmaceutical drugs. A wise person will search out natural remedies.

God has provided the herbs of the field for "the service of man."[30] Over the centuries, various people have discovered that certain natural plants have extraordinary healing qualities. If a person's thoughts, words, and actions are in harmony with God's way of life, he can expect these natural remedies to be effective.

An example of a natural remedy can be found in a recommendation that Paul gave Timothy. Apparently, Timothy suffered from continual stomach problems, so Paul gave him wise counsel to apply a natural treatment for his "often infirmities."[31] Today's application of his counsel would be grape juice, which is rich in antioxidants and very beneficial for stomach ailments.[32,33,34,35]

When King Hezekiah developed a sickness with the symptom of skin boils, he went to Isaiah for counsel. God told Isaiah that if the king would apply a compress of figs to the boils, he would recover.[36]

Today, millions of men suffer from the inability to have proper physical relations in marriage. As a result, they are buying drugs that often have damaging side effects. The Israelites understood a solution to this problem.[37]

When Elijah suffered from suicidal depression, God's cure was to put him into a deep sleep, awaken him to eat a wholesome meal with pure water, and cause him to go back to sleep and then repeat this process.[38]

There are hundreds of natural remedies that are a part of God's way of life. These should be evaluated and used after eliminating deadly stresses.

"He causeth the grass to grow for the cattle, and herb for the service of man: that he may bring forth food out of the earth."[39]

The acclaimed forerunner of health programs in America was Paul C. Bragg.

Paul Bragg taught millions of people the principles of eating nutritious food, eliminating toxic substances from the body, developing pH balance, and experiencing the wonders of fasting.

9

Factor 5: What We Inherit

Your entire physical being is determined by your DNA structures. These structures contain the genetic code for the development of every cell in your body. DNA chains were passed to you from your forefathers, and you pass them on to your children and their children for generations to come.

The implications of this are profound, especially regarding our relationship to Adam. At a molecular level, we all were actually a part of Adam when he transgressed. Thus Scripture is able to say that we all were a physical part of Adam, and in him we all sinned and, therefore died.[1]

"By one man sin entered into the world, and death by sin; and so death passed upon all men, for that all have sinned."[2]

A further example of this principle is in God's declaration that Levi paid tithes to Melchisedec even though those tithes were paid by Abraham hundreds of years before Levi was born. Yet God explains that because Levi was "in the loins" (reproductive potential) of Abraham, he technically participated in what Abraham did and thus received the benefits of Abraham's actions.[3]

Cause of Genetic Diseases

Each person has two copies of most of his genes. One copy is from his mother, while the other is from his father. A genetic disease results when one or both of these genes have a mutation.[4] This will affect cellular structure, resulting in congenital defects and diseases. Common genetic diseases are often traced to these mutations. They include hemophilia, cystic fibrosis, muscular dystrophy, and sickle cell anemia.

In addition to genetic diseases, every person inherits various weaknesses and tendencies toward certain diseases that "run in the family." By knowing that you have a low tolerance for certain diseases, you can develop personal disciplines to guard against them.

For example, if both parents have type 2 diabetes, their children will have an eighty percent risk of developing that disease.[5] These risks can be substantially reduced by diet and exercise.

Results of Genetic Diseases

Genetic diseases shorten the human life span. Our original forefathers lived for hundreds of years.

Our sin nature is inherited from our fathers. For this reason, Jesus had to be born of a virgin in order to be sinless and pay the penalty for our sin.

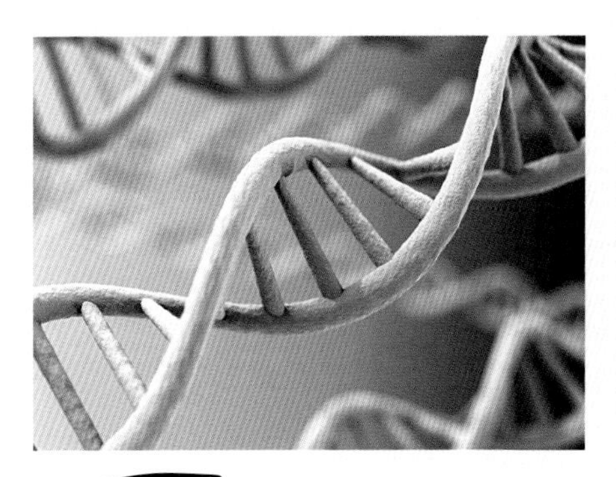

The DNA ladders that God created in Adam have continued to divide and multiply. Based on this, we were a part of Adam when he sinned and therefore suffer the consequences of his transgression.

"For as in Adam all die, even so in Christ shall all be made alive."[6]

Generational Iniquities

Abraham told a half-lie when he said of Sarah, "She is my sister."

Isaac told a full lie when he said of Rebekah, "She is my sister."

Jacob told a full lie and stole when he said, "I am Esau."

Jacob was deceived by his sons when they said, "Is this Joseph's coat?"

Today, it is unusual for a person to live more than one hundred years. This shortened life span is due to several factors, including impurities in our blood and damage to DNA structures over the centuries.[7]

Many people regard the phrase "threescore years and ten" as the Biblical life expectancy of a person. However, this phrase describes a shortened life span due to man's sins and iniquities: "Thou hast set our iniquities before thee, our secret sins in the light of thy countenance. For all our days are passed away in thy wrath: we spend our years as a tale that is told. The days of our years are [only] threescore years and ten; and if by reason of strength they be fourscore years, yet is their strength labor and sorrow."[8]

Treating Genetic Diseases

What we think, say, do, and eat will have a great effect on genetic diseases.[9,10] However, God often will use genetic conditions to carry out His great works in and through us.

When Jesus' disciples came upon a blind man, they asked Jesus, "Master, who did sin, this man, or his parents, that he was born blind?" Jesus answered, "Neither hath this man sinned, nor his parents: but that the works of God should be made manifest in him." Then Jesus healed the man's blindness, and multitudes glorified God.[11] Another example is the man who was lame from his mother's womb whom Peter and John healed.[12]

God's pattern is to form a person in the womb with all the capabilities he needs to carry out God's great works. In some cases, however, God withholds the key factor that a person needs, as in the case of Abraham's wife, Sarah. She was to be the mother of many nations, but she was barren.[13]

In these cases, it is exciting to follow the instruction of Scripture to call out to God for His supernatural work, bringing glory to His love and power: "Call unto me, and I will answer thee, and show thee great and mighty things, which thou knowest not."[14] The power of crying out has been used by many to deal with inherited defects.[15]

Sarah Hood

Sarah Hood was born with a congenital defect that caused her to have intense pain. She went to doctor after doctor for a solution. However, she received only toxic drugs, which produced further complications, and the pain became worse.

On her flight to our Total Health Seminar in March 2008, she wanted to tell the woman sitting next to her about the Lord. However, Sarah was doubled over with pain.

During the seminar, Sarah and her husband, Greg, learned that two pastors would be at the seminar on Thursday to anoint those who had incurable diseases and then to have the whole group cry out for their healing. Sarah asked that this be done for her.

By the next morning, Sarah's pain was totally gone. She was ecstatic and could not stop telling everyone what had happened. God healed her of pain she had suffered for more than fifty years!

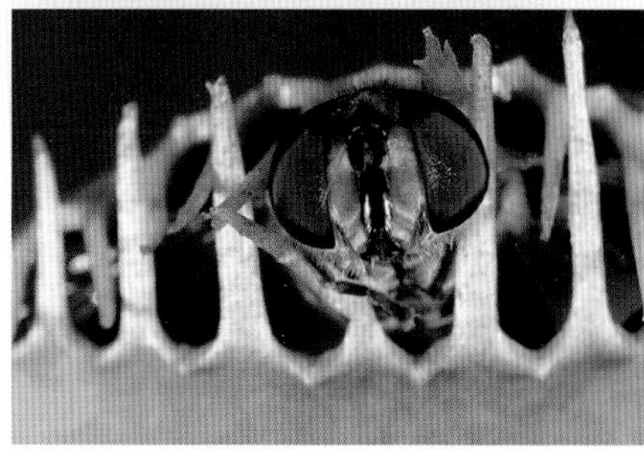

10

How Does Stress Cause Disease?

A Revolutionary Approach to Treating Diseases

Stress has long been recognized as a major contributor to sickness and disease.[1,2] It is therefore astonishing and unfortunate that the primary approach in treating diseases is to simply cover symptoms by prescribing drugs. Drugs may relieve some symptoms, but they will not address the root stresses that may cause or contribute to the diseases.

By taking this approach, the medical community is saying: "It does not really matter what you think, what you say, what you do, what you eat, or what you have inherited. Just take this drug, and you will feel better." However, the price of "feeling better" is often a new illness brought about by the side effects of the drug.[3,4] This then requires an additional drug, which may result in new diseases that require even more drugs.

In some cases, the drug that was designed to treat a condition actually intensifies the problem. This is the case regarding some antidepressants, which are now linked to a greater risk of suicide.[5]

A more effective approach would be to first determine the root causes and clear them up—then discuss diseases.

Tracing Diseases to Stress

Dr. Ryke Hamer is a German physician. In December 1978, his son died as a result of a gunshot wound. Dr. Hamer was overwhelmed with the grief and sorrow of this tragedy, and he soon developed cancer.

He wondered if there was any connection between his cancer and the unresolved stress of his grief. After conducting a study that involved more than twenty thousand patients, he was able to draw a direct correlation between various types of stress and specific diseases.

Dr. Hamer also observed that when a particular stress was resolved, the related disease often cleared up.

In 1981, Dr. Hamer presented his findings to the medical university from which he earned his degree in 1961. He was excited about the possibility of teaching this material at the university, because the purpose of his life was to find and eliminate the root causes of diseases.

After several months of silence, university officials informed him

The venus fly trap is like a stress—once it gets a hold of us, it eats us up. Thus what we eat is not as important as what eats us.

America's dairy consumption per capita is among the highest in the world. Yet Americans have more calcium deficiency than any other nation.[6]

Could this be due to stress? Calcium is vital for the proper functioning of such organs as the heart, brain, and kidneys. When stress depletes calcium, the body robs it from other sources such as the bones.

Dr. Alan Sivells

Scripture connects envy with bone diseases.[11]

Dr. Sivells writes: "I had so much pain in my shoulders that I could not lift my arms above my head. Often my wife had to help me dress in the morning.

"At a Total Health Seminar, I learned about the relationship between osteoporosis and envy. At first I did not think this applied to me until I realized that there was one area of envy I had. I cleared it up and also began to follow the practice of electrolyte balance. Nine days later, I felt completely well. I even played football for two hours with my boys, throwing overhand passes."

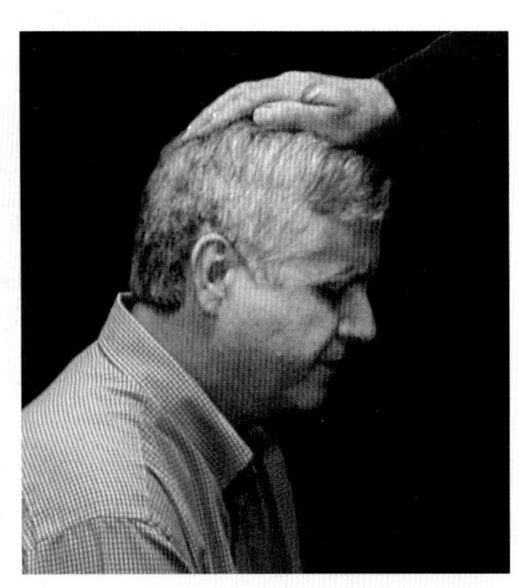

After Dr. Sivells confessed and rejected his envy, he was anointed with oil by elders in accordance with James 5:14–16.

that if he taught this information, they would see to it that his medical license was revoked.

After receiving their answer, Dr. Hamer decided that he could not turn his back on such overwhelming empirical data. Therefore, he began to share his medical findings with his patients.

As a result, his medical license was was revoked in 1986.[7] A major assault was then launched against him and his research.

The purpose of this book is not to try to validate or deny the results of Dr. Hamer's work. It is to explain how he gave us a key idea—the potential of researching specific stresses and how they directly relate to the systems of the body.

Our first step was to go to the powerful Sermon on the Mount that Jesus gave to the multitudes.

In that message, we identified seven basic stresses and their relationships to life.[8] These are anger, guilt, lust, bitterness, greed, fear, and envy.

When Jesus finished His message, those who had listened to Him were "astonished at his doctrine: For he taught them as one having authority."[9]

We also realized that there are seven primary systems of the human body.[10] The more we studied the seven stresses and the seven bodily systems, the more we saw an important correlation between them. For example, a person with anger is likely to suffer from heart problems. When a person has bitterness, he is likely to have digestive disorders.

As a growing number of individuals are now discovering this connection, they are recognizing how long-standing stresses are the root causes of their diseases. It is exciting to see that when these people resolve their stress, they often experience a dramatic healing from their disease.

Stresses Related to Bodily Systems

1. *Anger—the cardiovascular system*
2. *Guilt—the nervous system*
3. *Lust—the endocrine system*
4. *Bitterness—the digestive system*
5. *Greed—the immune system*
6. *Fear—the respiratory system*
7. *Envy—the musculoskeletal system*

Remember that there are four other factors of sickness and disease. Therefore, the fact that someone has a disease does not necessarily mean that he has the corresponding stress.

How Excess Cortisol Affects Health

Dr. Billica was the director of medical programs at NASA's Johnson Space Center in Houston, Texas, from 1991–2001. In this position, he was on the cutting edge of medical research for the purpose of keeping astronauts healthy while in space.

Roger Billica, M.D.

Dr. Billica describes in detail the damaging effects of stress on the hormonal systems of the body. He explains how stress causes an imbalance in cortisol levels, which, in turn, causes many health problems.

Cortisol is an antiinflammatory agent. It protects the body from inflammatory enzymes, excess histamines, and autoimmune substances. Cortisol also strengthens heart contractions and helps regulate the levels of sugar, sodium, and potassium in the blood.

In addition to throwing cortisol out of balance, stress causes the liver to make more glucose, which decreases dehydroepiandrosterone (DHEA). DHEA is an anabolic steroid that builds muscles, produces beneficial metabolic hormones, and releases antiaging hormones.

As stress increases, the thyroid slows down because it thinks that the body needs to conserve fuel. This alters the chemical process of methylation in the body, which causes an imbalance in the neurotransmitters, resulting in depression.

The imbalance of neurotransmitters, including serotonin depletion, also results in carbohydrate (sugar) craving. Increased sugar production combined with the carbohydrate craving causes increased insulin, insulin resistance syndrome, and diabetes.

There is also a decrease in cell energy, resulting in fatigue and muscle loss. The use of fat for energy is also inhibited, resulting in weight gain.[12]

How We Respond to Stress

The limbic system is located in the center of the brain and includes the hypothalamus and pituitary gland. It constantly receives and processes sensory input from the body.

Like a thermostat, the limbic system continually regulates bodily functions to maintain a constant balance.[13] It also acts as an emotional filing system, indexing memories by their value for future reference.[14]

The limbic system has a direct effect on the stress hormone system and influences the autonomic nervous system. When the limbic system perceives stress, neurotransmitters are released that begin a cascade of hormones. These hormones initially have beneficial purposes. However, when there is sustained or chronic stress, they become damaging.[15]

The autonomic nervous system, located outside the brain, also acts as a control center that is sensitive to stress.

Stress in the body is like powerful water that overflows its banks, causing damage.

Attitudes From Stress

Selfishness	*Disrespect*
Carelessness	*Unfriendliness*
Distraction	*Pride*
Self-centeredness	*Idleness*
Fearfulness	*Self-pity*
Rashness	*Fairness*
Indifference	*Infidelity*
Covetousness	*Anger*
Under-achievement	*Willfulness*
Double-mindedness	*Confusion*
	Restlessness
Offensiveness	*Contentiousness*
Inconsistency	*Tardiness*
Faintheartedness	*Wastefulness*
Slothfulness	*Unreliability*
Judgment	*Anxiety*
Simplemindedness	*Self-indulgence*
Discouragement	*Callousness*
Apathy	*Hypocrisy*
Unbelief	*Incompleteness*
Resistance	*Extravagance*
Bitterness	*Condemnation*
Stinginess	*Deception*
Harshness	*Weakness*
Murmuring	*Foolishness*

Dr. Joel Robbins

Dr. Robbins is a medical, chiropractic, and naturopathic doctor. He combines all three disciplines in his practice along with a thorough knowledge of Biblical principles in treating his patients. Stress often is the cause of his patients' diseases. Here is one of many examples.

"A lady in her thirties could hardly walk into my office because of the pain in her back.

"When I asked what happened, she said, 'I picked up a glass from the counter, and my back went out.' This woman had no history of back problems and had never had a previous backache.

"So I said to her, 'Why are you worrying about finances?' Her mouth dropped open and she said, 'How do you know?' I said, 'You told me it was not physically induced.' She then explained that her husband had been transferred overseas and she had not been able to sleep at night because of worries about their financial situation.

"We prayed, and she transferred the financial responsibility back to her husband and the Lord. Then she stood up with no pain in her back."

How Stress Causes Disease

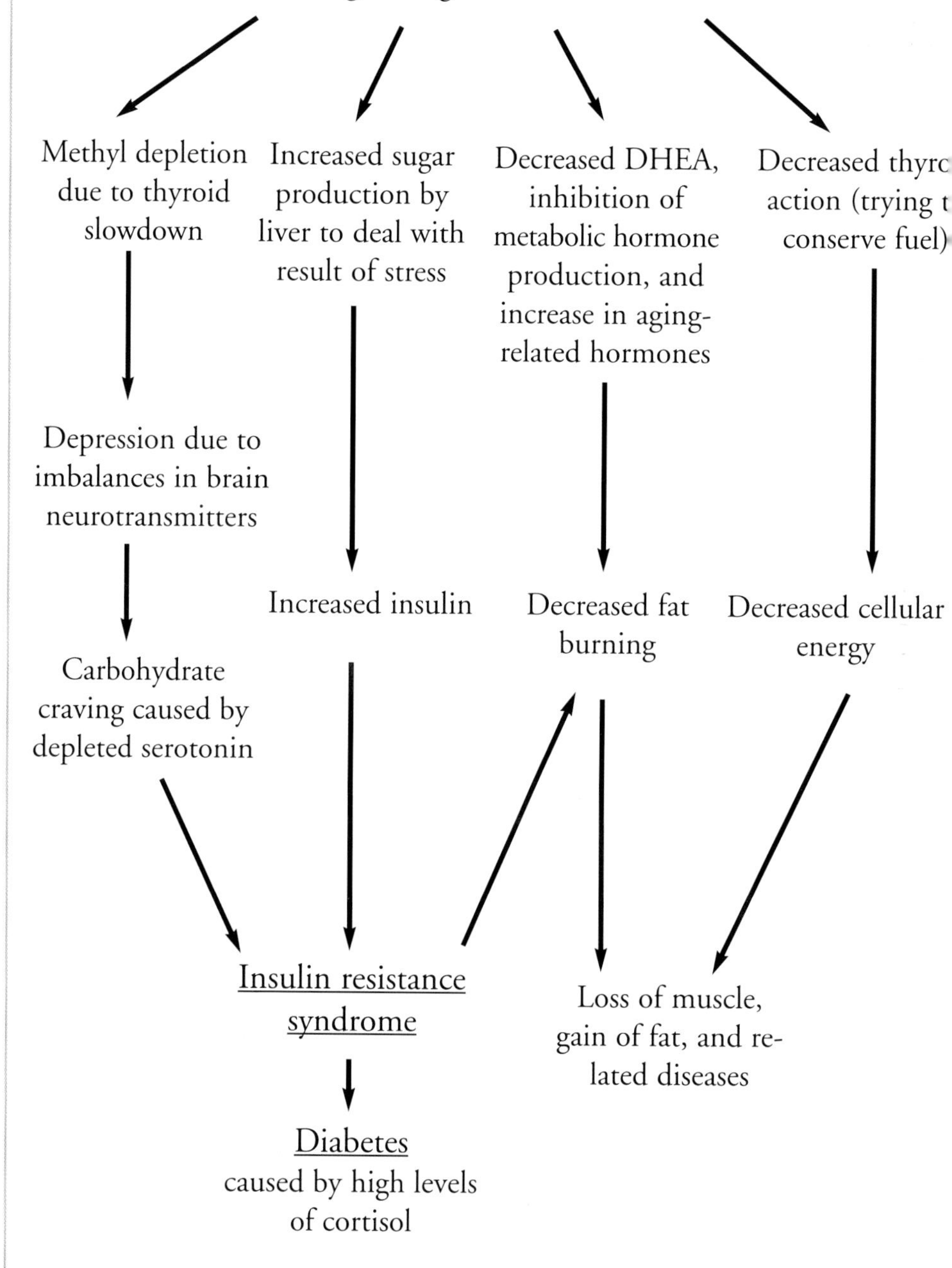

This chart is based on a lecture by Dr. Roger Billica.[16]

Resolving Stress

The magnificence of the human being is praised by the psalmist, who wrote, "I will praise thee; for I am fearfully and wonderfully made: marvelous are thy works; and that my soul knoweth right well."[17]

God designed us in such a way that if we violate His commands, we will experience the soul diseases of anger, guilt, lust, bitterness, greed, fear, and envy. However, God has promised that all of these diseases of the soul can be healed. "Bless the LORD, O my soul, and forget not all his benefits . . . who healeth all thy diseases."[18]

The healing comes by learning and applying the forty-nine commands that Jesus taught during His earthly ministry, which He commissioned us to share with all the nations of the world.

The Power Behind Character

When you carry out a command, you develop a character quality such as compassion, generosity, patience, initiative, gratefulness, hospitality, and forty-three more!

Each command, with its resulting character quality, is actually one of forty-nine practical ways to love God and others. What is even more exciting is that for each stress, there are seven commands that directly relate to it. Thus when the commands are applied, the stress is resolved and the physical symptoms often clear up.

The most powerful medicine in the world is love.

The famous thirteenth chapter of I Corinthians provides a definition of love. It is significant that it amplifies the seven stresses.

- **Love suffereth long and is kind (vs. anger).**
- **Love envieth not (vs. envy).**
- **Love vaunteth not itself and is not proud (vs. guilt).**
- **Love doth not behave itself unseemly (vs. lust).**
- **Love seeketh not her own (vs. greed).**
- **Love is not easily provoked (vs. bitterness).**
- **Love thinketh no evil (vs. fear).**

Applying Christ's Commands

1. Turn anger into the power of compassion.

1. Repent, for the kingdom of God is at hand. (See Matthew 4:17.)
2. Rejoice when men revile you. (See Matthew 5:11–12.)
3. Go to an offender and tell him his fault. (See Matthew 18:15.)
4. Love your enemies and bless those who curse you. (See Matthew 5:44–46.)
5. Be as perfect as your Father in heaven. (See Matthew 5:46–48.)
6. Honor your father and mother. (See Matthew 15:4.)
7. Go the second mile. (See Matthew 5:41.)

2. Replace guilt with inward peace.

1. Be born again. (See John 3:7.)
2. Love the Lord with all your heart, soul, mind, and strength. (See Matthew 22:37.)
3. Hear God's voice. (See Matthew 11:15.)
4. Properly observe communion. (See Matthew 26:26–27.)
5. Be reconciled to your brother. (See Matthew 5:23–25.)
6. Judge not so that you will not be judged. (See Matthew 7:1.)
7. Keep your word. (See Matthew 5:37.)

Courtesy of www.SolveFamilyProblems.com

If we keep Christ's commands, we can claim the following promises.

- **God will reveal Himself to us.**

"He that hath my commandments, and keepeth them, he it is that loveth me: and he that loveth me shall be loved of my Father, and I will love him, and will manifest myself to him."[19]

- **We will receive God's love.**

"If ye keep my commandments, ye shall abide in my love."[20]

- **We will know that we love God.**

"Hereby we do know that we know him, if we keep his commandments. . . . Whoso keepeth his word, in him verily is the love of God perfected: hereby know we that we are in him."[21]

- **Our prayers will be answered.**

"Whatsoever we ask, we receive of him, because we keep his commandments."[22]

- **God will dwell in us.**

"If a man love me, he will keep my words: and my Father will love him, and we will come unto him, and make our abode with him."[23]

- **Christ will be our Friend.**

"Ye are my friends, if ye do whatsoever I command you."[24]

3. Transform lust into the dynamic of genuine love.

1. Honor God's Law. (See Matthew 5:17.)
2. Do not commit adultery. (See Matthew 5:28.)
3. Practice secret disciplines. (See Matthew 6:1–18.)
4. Choose the narrow way. (See Matthew 7:13–14.)
5. Reject false prophets. (See Matthew 7:15–16.)
6. Beware of the leaven of the Pharisees. (See Matthew 16:6.)
7. Honor marriage. (See Matthew 19:4–6.)

4. Defeat bitterness with full forgiveness.

1. Await My return. (See Matthew 24:42–44.)
2. Deny yourself. (See Luke 9:23–25.)
3. Love your neighbor. (See Matthew 22:39.)
4. Be a servant. (See Matthew 20:27.)
5. Ask in faith. (See Matthew 21:21–22.)
6. Forgive offenders. (See Matthew 18:21.)
7. Despise not little ones. (See Matthew 18:10.)

5. Overcome greed with a spirit of generosity.

1. Let your light shine before men. (See Matthew 5:14–16.)
2. Lay up treasures in heaven. (See Matthew 6:19–21.)
3. Seek first the kingdom of God and His righteousness. (See Matthew 6:33.)
4. Beware of covetousness. (See Luke 12:15.)
5. Bring in the poor. (See Luke 14:12–14.)
6. Ask, seek, and knock. (See Matthew 7:7–8.)
7. Render to Caesar the things that are Caesar's. (See Matthew 22:19–21.)

6. Cast out fear with perfect love.

1. Follow Me, and I will make you fishers of men. (See Matthew 4:19.)
2. Take My yoke upon you, and learn of Me. (See Matthew 11:28–30.)
3. Be wise as serpents and harmless as doves. (See Matthew 10:16.)
4. Be a house of prayer. (See Matthew 21:13.)
5. Receive God's power. (See Luke 24:49.)
6. Watch and pray that you enter not into temptation. (See Matthew 26:41.)
7. Fear not those who kill only the body. (See Matthew 10:28.)

7. Conquer envy with sincere gratefulness.

1. Do to others what you would have them do to you. (See Matthew 7:12.)
2. Keep My commandments if you love Me. (See John 14:15.)
3. Feed My sheep. (See John 21:15–16.)
4. Baptize believers. (See Matthew 28:19.)
5. Make disciples. (See Matthew 28:20.)
6. Do not cast pearls before swine. (See Matthew 7:6.)
7. Pray for laborers. (See Matthew 9:37–38.)

Anger

How we deny or reveal anger

"I am not angry . . ."

"I am irritated."
"I am frustrated."
"I am out of patience."
"I am agitated."
"I am perturbed."
"I am disgusted."
"I am incensed."
"I am shocked."
"I am just tired."
"I am grouchy."
"I am 'righteously indignant.' "

Ways we reveal anger

A short temper
A raised voice
Contentious arguing
Punishing with silence
Pounding fists
Slamming doors
Using profanity
Glaring at others
A scowling look
Contempt or scorn
Sullen quietness
Sarcastic comments

How to Resolve

Anger

Required Command	Resulting Quality
Repent Matthew 4:17	**Humility** vs. Pride
Rejoice Matthew 5:11–12	**Joyfulness** vs. Self-Pity
Go to Offenders Matthew 18:15	**Justice** vs. Fairness
Love Your Enemies Matthew 5:44–46	**Creativity** vs. Underachievement
Be Perfect Matthew 5:46–48	**Sincerity** vs. Hypocrisy
Honor Parents Matthew 15:4	**Honor** vs. Disrespect
Go the Second Mile Matthew 5:38–42	**Deference** vs. Offensiveness

11

How Does Anger Affect the Cardiovascular System?

Heart disease is the number-one killer in America.[1] Almost half the deaths in the United States and Europe are caused by this condition. Cardiovascular disease claims the lives of more than two thousand Americans every twenty-four hours.[2]

The Cardiovascular System

The cardiovascular system is composed of the heart; the lymphatic ducts; and the blood vessels, which include the arteries, veins, and capillaries. These organs function together to maintain blood flow throughout every tissue of the body. Each excess pound of fat requires an extra mile of capillary tubing.[3]

The blood contains a mixture of life-sustaining electrolytes, red blood cells, white blood cells, proteins, platelets, and nutrients that are critical for every living cell.

The heart's primary function is to pump a steady flow of blood throughout the body to each cell.

The blood receives vital elements from the lungs, gastrointestinal organs, and bone marrow, and then carries away waste to the liver, kidney, and skin, where it is transformed and expelled from the body.

An Example of Anger Relating to Heart Failure

Anger has profound physiological effects on the cardiovascular system. This fact has been well documented.[4,5]

An illustration of this can be seen in the Biblical account of Nabal. He is described in Scripture as a very angry man. He was "churlish and evil in his doings."[6] The Hebrew word for *churlish* denotes all the bad qualities of anger—fierceness, cruelty, vehemence, stubbornness, etc.

When David protected Nabal's three thousand sheep all season and then asked for a reward, Nabal angrily "railed" against David's messengers and sent them away empty-handed.

That night, Nabal celebrated his prosperity by getting drunk. The next morning, when Nabal was sober, his wife told him how she had spared the family from death by giving David a reward for his work. As a result, Nabal's "heart died within him, and he became as a stone" and later died.[7]

Notice in this account that Nabal is described as an angry man. Thus he had repeated surges of adrenaline, which weakened his heart.

An outburst of anger is caused by the pent-up wrath from previous hurts that have not been resolved.

Wrath is cumulative. We "store up" wrath until it turns into bitterness and rage.

The eruption of a volcano not only causes great damage to the surrounding area but also spews into the atmosphere volcanic ash, which can literally go around the globe.

Harold Burr was a professor at the Yale School of Medicine for forty-three years. He is most well known for his claim that all living things are molded and controlled by electrodynamic fields—which he called fields of life or L-fields—that can be measured and mapped with standard voltmeters.

All cells generate electromagnetic messages much like a radio station. This energy can be measured in terms of electrodynamic fields. Experiments indicate that these fields can change as a result of stress.[17]

Based on Dr. Burr's research, stresses can alter the transmission of messages to other cells in the body and hinder their proper function.

A double-minded man is "like a wave of the sea driven with the wind and tossed. . . . Unstable in all his ways."[18]

How Anger Limits Circulation

The immediate result of anger is the release of adrenaline and cortisol. These hormones are powerful forces that increase the body's strength to flee a dangerous situation or fight off an attacker.

As adrenaline flows through the system, the veins and capillaries constrict to prevent profuse bleeding in case of wounds. This impairs circulation in the extremities. At the same time, the coronary arteries dilate to increase blood flow and oxygen to the vital organs, such as the muscles, brain, and heart.[8]

This response is designed only for emergencies. When it is overstimulated by anger, it produces high blood pressure, heart conditions, and a host of other problems.

To treat the resulting conditions without conquering the initial anger is futile. Scripture warns, "A man of great wrath shall suffer punishment: for if thou deliver him, yet thou must do it again."[9]

We see the association between anger and decreased circulation in extremities in the story of King Asa. A prophet reproved Asa for a very unwise decision. "Then Asa was wroth with the seer, and put him in a prison house; for he was in a rage with him because of this thing. And Asa oppressed some of the people the same time."[10]

The stress of King Asa's anger took its toll. Soon he developed a disease in his feet. Since he was angry at the prophet, he decided to go to the doctors for relief. The root problem, however, was not in his feet but in his heart. Because he failed to deal with this cause, "his disease was exceeding great," and he soon died.[11]

Lack of circulation often leads to foot disease. This likely was the cause of Asa's condition.

The Connection Between Anger and Heart Disease

One of the primary factors in heart disease is the buildup of plaque on the inner walls of the arteries. This condition, called atherosclerosis, narrows the vessels and ultimately can lead to serious blockage.

Atherosclerosis is the consequence of the body's repeated effort to heal damage to the lining of the artery, which is caused by such things as high blood pressure.[12] As we know, unresolved anger results in constriction of the arteries and elevation in blood pressure.

Atherosclerosis has been linked to elevated cholesterol.[13] However, the cholesterol alone is not the problem. Rather, it is the increased inflammation from oxidized cholesterol that results in scarring and excess plaque formation.[14]

The elevated cortisol that is produced by the stress of anger increases this oxidation of cholesterol.[15] The resulting buildup of plaque not only hardens the arteries but also narrows the channel through which blood can flow. The obvious result is higher blood pressure, which only further increases the problem.

A Harvard Medical School study has linked anger with a doubling of the risk of heart attack.[16]

How to Turn Anger Into the Power of Compassion

"Wrath is cruel, and anger is outrageous."[19] Because anger is so widespread and destructive, it is the first stress that Jesus mentions in His Sermon on the Mount. Anger not only damages the body, soul, and spirit, but it also destroys vital relationships, especially between marriage partners and family members.

When a father becomes angry, he may get over it within a few minutes, but the wounds to his wife and children continue to hurt and cause ever-deepening resentment and, eventually, bitterness.

Check for disease symptoms of anger.

Anger produces many different diseases that are related to the cardiovascular system. These include conditions such as high blood pressure, buildup of arterial plaque, deep vein thrombosis, poor circulation due to blood thickening, heart arrythmias, heart attacks, and strokes.

Recognize different forms of anger.

Many angry people deny their anger. They will, however, admit that they are frustrated, deeply hurt, or greatly offended by certain people or situations.

One mild-mannered man reported that he was taking medication for high blood pressure. This medication was causing damaging side effects, and his condition was growing worse.

When he was asked if he had a problem with anger, both he and his wife said no. But then he was asked, "Do you ever get irritated?" and both exclaimed, "Yes! All the time!"

He simply held his anger inside. His hormonal system could not distinguish between outward anger and inward frustration. Thus he suffered the consequences of anger in his cardiovascular system.

- ☐ **Are you frustrated with certain people?**
- ☐ **Do you get irritated by situations?**
- ☐ **Are you harboring deep hurts and emotional wounds?**
- ☐ **Have you taken up offenses for other people?**
- ☐ **Do you react sharply to the wrongs of others?**
- ☐ **Do you desire to get even with those who hurt you?**

Ask God for the desire and power (grace) to turn the stress of anger into genuine love. Among the forty-nine commands of love that the Lord Jesus Christ taught and demonstrated to His disciples, seven directly apply to overcoming anger.

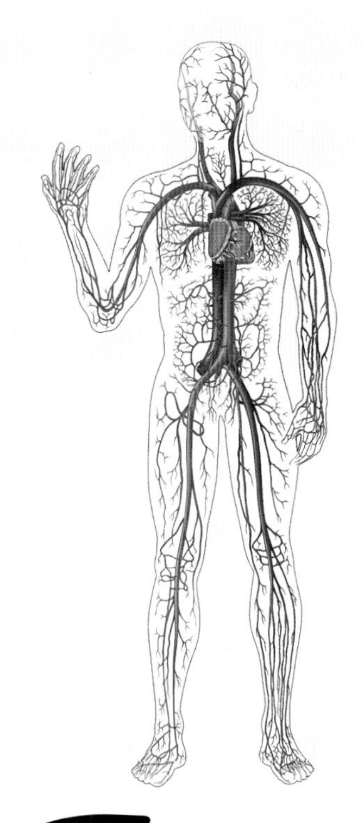

The cardiovascular system is composed of the heart, the lymphatic ducts, and the blood vessels, which include the arteries, veins, and capillaries.

Just as poisons build up in the body, so anger and wrath build up in the soul.

"But after thy hardness and impenitent heart treasurest up unto thyself wrath against the day of wrath."[20]

The kingdom of God has two phases—a future kingdom over all nations and a present kingdom over the hearts, souls, minds, and strength of believers.

There are five basic aspects of a kingdom.

1. **A king**
   The Lord Jesus Christ
2. **A jurisdictional boundary**
   Our whole hearts
3. **A law system**
   Christ's commands
4. **A loyal citizenry**
   Obedient disciples
5. **An opposing kingdom**
   The kingdom of darkness

Seven Commands to Conquer Anger

1. Repent

"Repent: for the kingdom of heaven is at hand."[21]

Resulting Quality: **Humility**

Anger is an expression of pride, because "Only by pride cometh contention."[22] "God resisteth the proud, but giveth grace unto the humble."[23] Anger indicates that you have centered your life around what pleases or displeases you rather than what pleases or displeases God.

Anger stems from unyielded rights and expectations.

Anger is the evidence that someone has found and overstepped personal rights that you have claimed for yourself but that you should have entrusted to God. Anger further reveals expectations from people or things that should ultimately be placed only on God. Thus David prayed, "My soul, wait thou only upon God; for my expectation is from him."[24]

Anger is simply one evidence that you are trying to run your own life with your own energy, and people or situations are getting in the way of you reaching your goals and ambitions.

Repentance is restoring relationships.

Repentance is not just sorrow over the consequences of your sins; it is grief over a broken relationship with God. As David said, "Against thee, thee only, have I sinned, and done this evil in thy sight."[25]

Esau "found no place of repentance, though he sought it carefully with tears."[26] He was grieved only over the blessings he lost by selling his birthright. David had true repentance and forgiveness for his adultery and murder because he grieved over his broken relationship with God.[27]

Personal Application

- ☐ Would the people who live with me say that I get angry?
- ☐ Am I truly grieved over my broken relationship with God?
- ☐ Do I realize that when I cause offense in others, I am sinning against God? Jesus said, "Inasmuch as ye have done it unto one of the least of these my brethren, ye have done it unto me."[28] When Saul persecuted believers, Jesus said, "I am Jesus whom thou persecutest."[29]
- ☐ Am I trying to run my life for my own benefit rather than acknowledging the Lord Jesus as the sovereign Ruler of my life and yielding to Him all my rights and expectations?

2. Rejoice

"Blessed are ye, when men . . . say all manner of evil against you falsely, for my sake. Rejoice."[30]

Resulting Quality: Joyfulness

Your first response to an irritating situation must not be anger but rather thankfulness: "Rejoice evermore. . . . In every thing give thanks: for this is the will of God in Christ Jesus concerning you."[31]

Thanking God is different from being thankful. To thank God for allowing a situation is an action of the will based on the promise that "All things work together for good to them that love God, to them who are the called according to his purpose."[32]

Discover why God let it happen.

Joyfulness is a condition of the spirit. This begins when you list the benefits that God intended when He allowed a situation to happen. The first benefit is the development of character qualities that will conform you to the character of Christ. These include humility, compassion for others, and patience, because "tribulation worketh patience; and patience, experience; and experience, hope."[33]

Realize that God writes last chapters.

God designed you to accomplish great works for Him; but to do them, you must go through character-shaping persecution. Paul writes, "If we suffer, we shall also reign with him."[34] Thus "It is good for a man that he bear the yoke in his youth. . . . He giveth his cheek to him that smiteth him: he is filled full with reproach."[35]

Therefore, you can rejoice when all men speak evil against you falsely, "for so persecuted they the prophets which were before you."[36]

Personal Application

- ☐ Do I realize that nothing can happen to me except what God allows for His purposes? Therefore, I can rejoice and thank Him for all things.
- ☐ God is not interested in protecting my reputation but His. Have I therefore purposed to represent Him and protect His reputation?
- ☐ Have I learned the skill of listing God's intended benefits for even the worst tragedies that could happen to me?
- ☐ Have I checked to make sure that I am suffering for Jesus' sake and not for my own sake because of anger, irritations, wrong attitudes, failure to fulfill responsibilities, or lack of love?

Anger begins as a small flame.

If not put out, anger turns into wrath, which is like a bonfire.

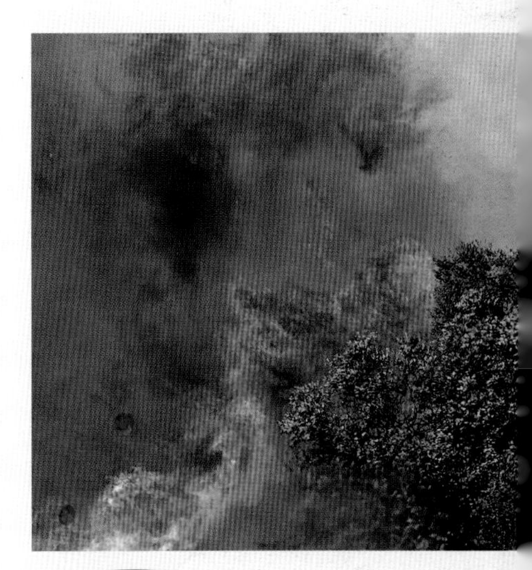

Finally, it becomes malice, which is like a raging forest fire.

By going directly to our offenders, we are able to discover the motivation that prompted their offense toward us.

- Our lack of love for them
- A prideful attitude in us
- Misunderstanding our motives
- Wrong words we said
- Wrong deeds we did
- Failure to fulfill our duties
- Unrealistic expectations of us
- Our offenses against their friends
- Basic needs in their lives
- Reaction to our standards
- Association with one they dislike
- A "cry" for our help

Based on all these possibilities, we should go to offenders with a humble and teachable attitude.

"Where no wood is, there the fire goeth out: so where there is no talebearer, the strife ceaseth."[40]

3. Go to Offenders

"If thy brother shall trespass against thee, go and tell him his fault between thee and him alone."[37]

Resulting Quality: Justice

When someone offends you, your natural response is to get angry and tell you friends how you were offended and who did it. This immediately violates this command!

When you tell other people about an offense before going to the offender to check out the facts, you can be sure that you will tell only your side of the story. You can also be certain that there is another side. Thus Scripture states, "He that is first in his own cause seemeth just; but his neighbor cometh and searcheth him."[38]

Narrow the circle of offense.

By telling others what your offender has done, you cause them to sin by judging your offender without knowing all the facts. You also motivate them to take up an offense against that person for you. Judging another person is a violation of a command of Christ, and taking up an offense is a further violation of Scripture. We are not to judge others, and we are not to take up an offense for others. "He that backbiteth not with his tongue, nor doeth evil to his neighbor, nor taketh up a reproach against his neighbor. . . . He that doeth these things shall never be moved."[39]

Those whom you tell will not just hear your words but also interpret your tonal patterns, angry emotions, facial expressions, and other body language. They will then tell others about the offense based on their complete interpretation. This will usually be a distorted, exaggerated, and inaccurate report that will likely get back to your offender. When he hears about the "lies" you are spreading, he will have new reasons to dislike you and do to you what you did to him.

Personal Application

- ☐ Do I tend to tell others about the offenses that happen to me before going to the offender and checking out the facts?
- ☐ Has telling others about the offense caused my offender to become angry over "false statements" that are getting back to him?
- ☐ When I go to an offender, do I have a humble and teachable spirit, or do I go in anger and create a greater reaction toward me?
- ☐ If I have caused reaction and divisions by prematurely sharing offenses, should I ask forgiveness of those I have offended?

4. Love Your Enemies

"Bless them that curse you, do good to them that hate you, and pray for them which despitefully use you, and persecute you."[41]

Resulting Quality: Creativity

It is impossible to remain angry with someone you genuinely love. But how is it possible to love someone who is your enemy? In this command, God gives three practical steps of action. When you follow them, you will experience a change in your heart, which is likely to trigger a changed response toward you in the heart of your enemy.

Give a verbal blessing.

To bless your enemy is to ask God to build in his life the character qualities that are missing. These might include humility, compassion, kindness, generosity, etc. When you verbally ask God to bless your enemies, you impart to them a divine power (grace) that enables them to develop these qualities. You also neutralize the hurtful emotions that you have experienced because of their words or actions.

Do good.

After blessing your enemies, you should look for ways to do good works for their benefit. As you invest your time, energy, and money into these good works, you will begin to actually love your enemies, because "where your treasure is, there will your heart be also."[42]

Pray fervently.

"Death and life are in the power of the tongue."[43] Therefore, as you pray for your enemies, you allow God to work in their lives as He promises: "The effectual fervent prayer of a righteous man availeth much."[44]

Personal Application

- ☐ How many of my enemies were made because of personal faults, failures, and blind spots?
- ☐ Have I determined the character qualities that are lacking in my enemies, and have I asked God to bless them with these qualities?
- ☐ Have I used creativity to design practical and appropriate gifts or services that I can give to express God's love?
- ☐ Have I asked God for the grace to pray for my enemies from a heart that is energized by God's love and my faith?

Unwise words are like deadly traps that hold our souls in bondage.

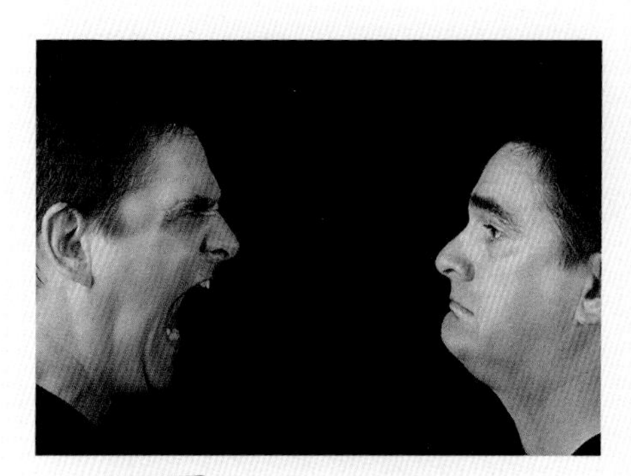

It is hurtful when enemies offend us with wrong actions. It is even more hurtful when we cause our own offense with wrong responses.

God's love through us is like the warmth of sunshine that melts the icy hearts of our enemies.

5. Be Perfect

"Be ye therefore perfect, even as your Father which is in heaven is perfect."[45]

Resulting Quality: **Sincerity**

To be perfect [*téleios*] is to be mature, fully grown, and fulfilling our potential.

A salute should be more than an outward gesture. It is a sincere embrace with our hearts of those we meet.

There is no partiality in the sunshine and rain God gives. Neither should we show prejudice in the greetings we give.

You have probably heard the statement "nobody is perfect" and assumed that it is true. Why, then, would God command us to be perfect? To make it even more difficult, we are to have the same perfection as that of our heavenly Father!

Greet everyone enthusiastically!

Jesus relates "perfection" to the way we greet people. When you see a close friend, your eyes brighten up, you smile at him, and you greet him with joy and enthusiasm. God wants us all to give this kind of greeting to every single person we meet! "If ye love them which love you, what reward have ye? do not even the publicans the same? And if ye salute your brethren only, what do ye more than others? do not even the publicans so? Be ye therefore perfect, even as your Father which is in heaven is perfect."[46] How is God "perfect" in this context? "He maketh his sun to rise on the evil and on the good, and sendeth rain on the just and on the unjust."[47]

You have only one opportunity to make a first impression. The instant someone makes eye contact with you, he will immediately discern your attitudes toward him.

If he sees no warm smile or bright eye contact, he will assume that you do not value him as an important person. He will sense rejection from you, and he will put up a wall to protect himself. This will cut off any opportunity for you to tell him about a loving Savior. Most people have been deeply hurt by rejection and are very sensitive to it. This is why an enthusiastic "salute" is so vital and so powerful.

Personal Application

- ☐ Do I salute those who have offended me with the same enthusiastic greeting that I give my closest friends?
- ☐ When I approach another person, do I remember that I have only one opportunity to give that person a first impression of God's love?
- ☐ When I see a person, do I look past any distractions of their physical appearance so that I can smile warmly into their hearts?
- ☐ When I greet someone enthusiastically and they want to talk further, do I have questions I can ask to find common ground?

6. Honor Parents

"Honor thy father and mother."[48]

Resulting Quality: **Honor**

The relationship you have with your parents will affect every other relationship in life, either for good or for bad. No wonder God made this the first command with a promise attached to it.

If you honor your parents, things will go well for you, and you will enjoy good health and long life. If you dishonor them, things will not go well for you, and it will affect your health and life expectancy.

Comprehend the seriousness of blessings and curses.

When it comes to blessings and curses, it is certainly true that "Death and life are in the power of the tongue"![49]

Isaac gave a verbal blessing to Jacob, and God honored it. Jacob unknowingly put a curse on his favorite wife, Rachel, and she died in childbirth. Samuel cursed Saul, and Saul cursed his courageous son Jonathan. Both Saul and Jonathan died in battle.

God's Law required that anyone who hit his parents or cursed them be stoned to death by all the fathers in the city! This would abruptly stop the juvenile delinquency in the nation.

Discern the nature of a curse.

There are several Hebrew words for *curse.* They range from a mild disrespect to a violent consignment to hell. The word that God used in the law that required stoning of those who cursed their parents is the term for mild disrespect! Jesus affirmed this law when He condemned the Pharisees for using their traditions to avoid giving their parents proper honor.

Personal Application

- ☐ Have I discerned qualities my parents lack that cause me to dishonor them? Have I asked God to bless them with these qualities?
- ☐ Have I asked my parents to point out qualities I need to develop and asked my father to give me a verbal blessing for their development?
- ☐ Do I have any friends who do not honor their parents and discourage me from honoring my parents?
- ☐ Do I listen to music, engage in activities, or wear any clothes that do not honor my parents' wishes?
- ☐ Have I purposed not to court or marry without the full blessing of both sets of parents?

Ravens eat dead animals. To confirm that an animal is dead, they first peck out its eyes.

"The eye that mocketh at his father, and despiseth to obey his mother, the ravens of the valley shall pick it out,and the young eagles shall eat it."[50]

Courtesy of www.SolveFamilyProblems.com

Jacob realized that the most important factor for the success of his life was the blessing of his father. Thus he did whatever he needed to do to obtain it.

Our hearts follow our treasures. If we invest them in offenders, we will automatically begin to love them.

"For where your treasure is, there will your heart be also."[52]

By going the first mile, we discharge our responsibility. By going the second mile, we meet a friend. Witnessing usually begins on the second mile.

7. Go the Second Mile

"Whosoever shall compel thee to go a mile, go with him twain."[51]

Resulting Quality: Deference

It is difficult to imagine the deep hatred that the Jewish people had toward the Roman soldiers who ruled over their nation. The hatred was most likely fueled by the law that required any male over the age of twelve to carry a soldier's heavy pack one mile in any direction.

Thus the command to go a second mile would have been a shock to the Jewish ears! However, Jesus understood human nature—He designed it! He knows that when we act voluntarily, our whole attitude changes.

Recognize the rewards of the second mile.

Picture a fifteen-year-old Jewish boy who was commanded by a gruff Roman soldier to carry his heavy military pack for one mile. During that mile, he remembered Jesus' command to go a second mile.

When he offered to carry the pack a second mile, the surprised soldier asked him why. The young man was then able to explain the teachings of Jesus. The time passed quickly, and at the end of the second mile, the soldier thanked him for his words and his help. They exchanged warm smiles as they shook hands. As the boy returned, he realized what had happened. "I walked a mile and discharged my duty. I walked a second mile and met a friend!"

A patient with severe mid-back pain visited Dr. Joel Robbins for treatment. Dr. Robbins adjusted his back three times, but there was no improvement. So he asked his patient about stress. His patient replied, "I was just granted a divorce, and the judge has ordered that I pay my wife more than I think is fair." Dr. Robbins suggested, "Why don't you write out a check for that amount and add some more to it?" A week later, the patient returned and said: "I thought you were the craziest person I had ever met. But I did what you said, and my back pain is all gone."

Personal Application

- ☐ What obligations do I have that cause me to be irritated or angry?
- ☐ How can I do more than is required to fulfill these duties?
- ☐ What answer will I give when I cheerfully go the second mile and am asked, Why are you doing this? A good answer would be, I am doing this to show my love for Jesus and His love for you!
- ☐ What treasures can I invest in the lives of my enemies?

Guilt

How we deny or reveal guilt

"I am not guilty . . ."

"Everyone does it."
"They are mostly at fault."
"I don't see why it's wrong."
"They are too touchy."
"I was just having fun."
"Can't you take a joke?"
"It was such a tiny thing."
"No one will ever know."
"My parents let me do it."
"Others made me do it."
"I did not have any choice."

Ways we reveal guilt

Blaming others
Excessive shyness
Avoiding eye contact
Shortness of breath
Verbal fillers (um/ah)
Excessive twitching/blinking
Nervous laughter
Harshness toward others
Exaggerating facts
Paralyzing fear
Bouts of depression

How to Resolve

Guilt

Required Command	Resulting Quality
Be Born Again John 3:7	**Security** vs. Anxiety
Love the Lord Matthew 22:37–38	**Enthusiasm** vs. Apathy
Hear God's Voice Matthew 11:15	**Attentiveness** vs. Distraction
Observe Communion Matthew 26:26–27	**Thoroughness** vs. Incompleteness
Be Reconciled Matthew 5:23–25	**Responsibility** vs. Unreliability
Judge Not Matthew 7:1–3	**Discernment** vs. Judgment
Keep Your Word Matthew 5:37	**Truthfulness** vs. Deception

12

How Does Guilt Affect the Nervous System?

Guilt is a continuous stress that affects the central nervous system. The result is manifested in voluntary and involuntary responses—physically, mentally, emotionally, and spiritually.

The Nervous System

The nervous system is a complex network of highly specialized cells. Its primary purpose is to maintain continuous communication with every living cell in the body.

In the same way that imbalance in the nervous system impairs communication, so guilt in the conscience destroys our ability to communicate with the Spirit of God and the spirits of others.[1]

The basic functional unit of the nervous system is the neuron, which operates through electrical signaling and neurotransmitters. These signals are fired at speeds of up to 120 meters per second.[2] This permits coordination of responses in the brain and throughout the body.

The nervous system handles a continuous flow of information that gives us a constant awareness of both our internal and external environments. The nervous system is composed of three major parts. The first is the sensory neurons, which carry information into the second part, the central nervous system (CNS). This is the command center of the body. From there, motor neurons carry out the commands of the CNS and control such things as strength, intestinal movement, secretions, blood pressure, and many other organ functions.

Damaged nervous tissue has a limited ability to regenerate or replace itself. This can lead to serious consequences.[3] A similar effect is experienced when the conscience is damaged with sustained guilt.

What Is Guilt?

Guilt presupposes an unchangeable, universal standard of right and wrong—good and evil. The evidence of this is in the Law of God, which He has placed in the heart of every person.

Scripture states that all people "show the work of the law written in their hearts, their conscience also bearing witness, and their thoughts the mean while accusing or else excusing one another."[4]

Sin is failure to measure up to the standard of this Law. This is the condition of every person, "For all have sinned, and come short of the glory of God."[5]

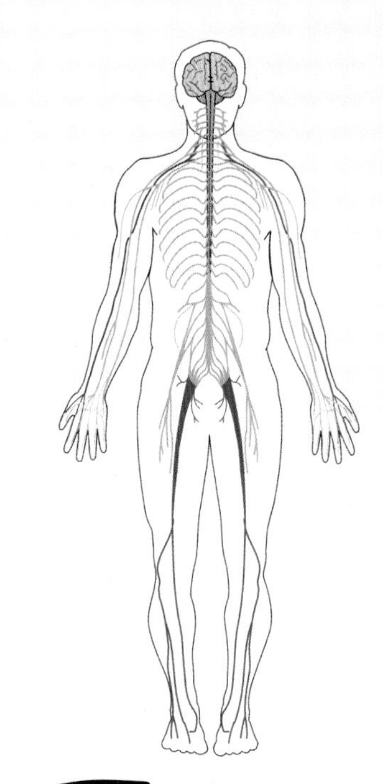

The nervous system has three major parts. Sensory neurons carry information to the CNS. Then motor neurons carry out commands.

The human soul and spirit function in the same way. The spirit brings information to the conscience, and the conscience gives direction for actions.

God warns that without a clear conscience, we will make shipwreck of our faith.[6]

The trial by bitter water was designed by God to expose the guilt of secret sin.[17]

If an Israelite wife was accused by her husband of being unfaithful to him and she denied it, he was to take her before the priests, and she was required to drink a cup of water mixed with the (impure) dust from the Tabernacle floor.

If she was innocent, it would not hurt her, because her immune system would protect her. If she was guilty, it would rot her thigh.

A clear conscience is being able to look every person in the eye and know that none can say, "You offended me, and you never tried to make it right."

Transgression is exceeding the limits of God's Law, as Adam did in the Garden of Eden. Paul reasoned, "Where no law is, there is no transgression."[7]

Iniquity is doing our own will, even if it appears to be good. Jesus explained: "Many will say to me in that day, Lord, Lord, have we not prophesied in thy name? and in thy name have cast out devils? and in thy name done many wonderful works? And then will I profess unto them, I never knew you: depart from me, ye that work iniquity."[8]

In Isaiah we read, "All we like sheep have gone astray; we have turned every one to his own way; and the LORD hath laid on him the iniquity of us all."[9]

Responses to Sin

Guilt is a powerful force in the mind, will, and emotions. It demands a response, and people deal with it in many different ways. Here is a list of examples we have from Scripture.

☐ **Covering Up Sin**

When Adam and Eve sinned, they lost their covering of light and saw themselves as naked. In an attempt to cover their nakedness, they sewed fig leaves together.[10]

This was not adequate for them, nor will it be effective for us, for "He that covereth his sins shall not prosper: but whoso confesseth and forsaketh them shall have mercy."[11]

☐ **Avoiding God's Presence**

When Adam and Eve heard God's voice in the garden, they hid from God even though they had covered themselves with fig leaves.[12] They knew that they had lost their glory and that God would realize immediately what they had done. The guilt of some people causes them to not only avoid God's presence but also deny His existence. Others change the reality of God into an image of their own imaginations. They "changed the glory of the uncorruptible God into an image made like to corruptible man."[13]

☐ **Blaming Others**

When God confronted Adam and Eve with their sin, they both passed the blame on to others and ultimately to God. Adam blamed God for the woman He had given him, and Eve blamed the serpent for beguiling her.[14] The implication was that because God had created the snake, He was responsible for what the snake did.

☐ **Denying Sin**

When Samuel confronted King Saul with accusations of disobedience, Saul denied it: "Wherefore then didst thou not obey the voice of the LORD, but didst fly upon the spoil, and didst evil in the sight of the LORD? And Saul said unto Samuel, Yea, I have obeyed the voice of the LORD, and have gone the way which the LORD sent me."[15] It is a natural response to deny that we have sinned, because then we feel that we do not need to deal with it.

☐ **Justifying Sin**

When Saul claimed that he had obeyed the Lord, he justified what he had done: "Blessed be thou of the LORD: I have performed the commandment of the LORD. . . . For the people spared the best of the sheep and of the oxen, to sacrifice unto the LORD thy God; and the rest we have utterly destroyed."[16]

It is said of criminals that everyone justifies what he has done and, therefore, is innocent in his own mind.

☐ Lying About Sin

When Elisha's servant, Gehazi, saw that Elisha refused to take any rewards for Naaman's healing, he ran after Naaman and told several lies in order to get some money. When he returned, Elisha asked him where he had been. Gehazi said, "Thy servant went no whither."[18]

Notice the further lies that had to be told in order to cover up his deception. First of all, he claimed to be a servant of Elisha, but he was really serving himself. Secondly, he did go somewhere, contrary to what he claimed. Sin leads to more sin, and deception leads to more deception.

☐ Giving Deceptive Answers

After Cain killed Abel, God asked Cain, "Where is Abel thy brother?" Rather than acknowledging that he had murdered him, Cain tried to sidestep the issue with a false answer and a distracting question: "I know not: am I my brother's keeper?"[19] This is a common tactic used by those who live with guilt.

☐ Judging Other People

When guilt sets in for sins that a person has committed, his reticular activating system goes into effect, and he becomes alert to other people who appear to be guilty of similar sins. Whether they are guilty or not, the person will judge them.

However, Scripture points out, "Thou art inexcusable, O man, whosoever thou art that judgest: for wherein thou judgest another, thou condemnest thyself; for thou that judgest doest the same things."[20]

☐ Reacting to the Message

When Asa failed to follow God's direction, and the prophet brought the failure to Asa's attention, Asa became angry at the prophet rather than humbling himself and acknowledging that he was wrong.[21]

☐ Punishing the Messenger

After King Asa reacted to the message that the prophet brought to him from God, he put the prophet in prison. He did not like the message, so he banished the messenger. It is a common response of guilt to attack the character and validity of the messenger if the guilty person does not like the message.

☐ Being Too Harsh

When Nathan confronted David about his sin, he told David a story of a rich man who had stolen a neighbor's sheep. The Law made it clear that such a theft would require a payment of four sheep.[22]

However, David became angry and demanded that the man pay back four sheep and then be killed. He was obviously reacting to his own guilt. Nathan said, "Thou art the man."[23]

☐ Being Too Lenient

If a guilty person is not overly strict, he will tend to be too lenient in dealing with those who have committed similar sins.

Eli violated God's Law in regard to the sacrifices. Therefore, he was unable to restrain his sons from their immorality. God judged him and his sons with death.[24] Similarly, David was not able to discipline his oldest son

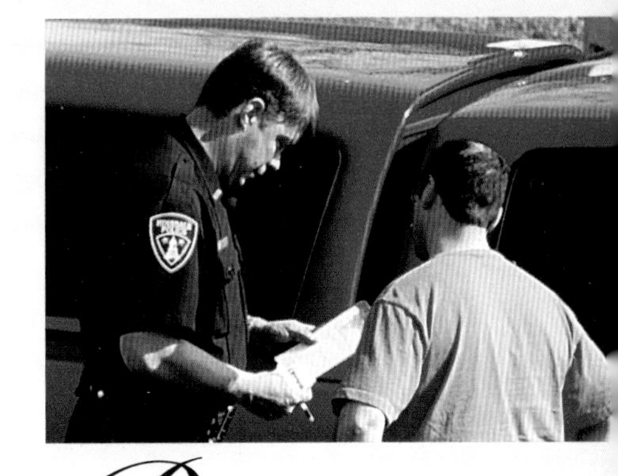

Police are trained to detect physical signs of guilt.

- ☐ Blinking
- ☐ Twitching or flinching
- ☐ Folding arms or crossing legs
- ☐ Lightly touching nose or eyes
- ☐ Raising tone and pitch of voice
- ☐ Looking away from speaker
- ☐ Nervous laughter or coughing
- ☐ Squinting eyes
- ☐ Putting head at an angle
- ☐ Increasing breathing rate
- ☐ Blushing or flushed skin
- ☐ Verbal fillers (um, uh, etc.)
- ☐ Long pauses before answering

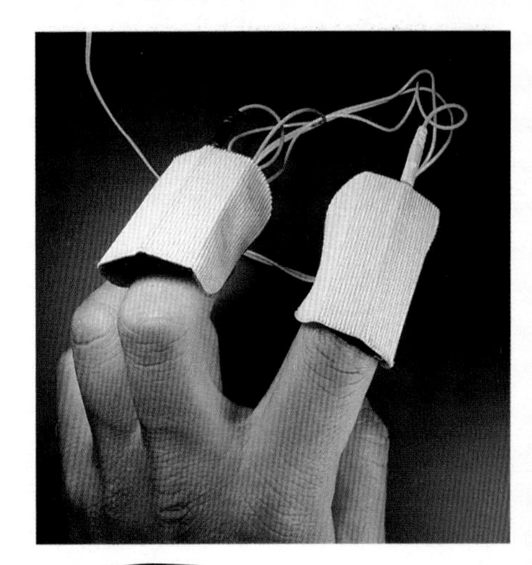

The polygraph test affirms the effect of guilt on the whole body by measuring changes.

Guilt is like a leak in an "emotional bucket." When the bucket is empty, depression results.

Courtesy of www.SolveFamilyProblems.com

We can use up our emotional energy on great works like Elijah's revival on Mount Carmel, or we can use it up on the guilt of secret sins.

Courtesy of www.SolveFamilyProblems.com

Jonah's depression was caused by his emotional drain from the revival of Nineveh, his guilt over running from God, and his anger at God!

for his immoral actions with his half-sister. Therefore, Absalom did it for him by killing his brother.[25]

☐ **Finding Wrong Support**

Those who have guilt are able to quickly identify others who are also guilty. They form quick, strong, and long-lasting soul ties, because they have a common bond. They also infect each other with their evil ways and desires.[26]

What Is Depression?

From a practical standpoint, depression is simply the result of running out of emotional energy. It can be used up on either good or bad activities.

Elijah and Jonah used up their emotional energy to bring about national revivals. In both cases, this was followed by suicidal depression.[27] Similarly, a mother who gives birth to a child may experience postpartum depression.

Guilt is a continual drain on emotional energy. Sooner or later, it will bring about depression and all the accompanying emotional, mental, physical, and spiritual consequences.

Depression Caused by Guilt

The medical community has not been able to precisely identify the cause of depression. However, they do understand that it relates to a deficiency in the neurotransmitters of the nervous system. Thus they treat it as a chemical imbalance.[28] This deficiency results in abnormal thoughts, erratic emotions, and physical manifestations such as fatigue, insomnia, restlessness, and decreased appetite.

In a given year, depressive disorders affect approximately 18.8 million American adults, or about 9.5% of the U.S. population aged 18 and older.[29] It is currently projected that, by 2020, depression will be the second-largest killer after heart disease![30]

The standard treatment for depression primarily involves the use of pharmaceutical drugs. However, studies have shown that antidepressants can actually intensify and complicate depression.[31] In fact, several antidepressants are linked to a greater risk of suicide.[32,33]

After researching the results from roughly forty studies of six popular antidepressants (SSRIs: selective serotonin reuptake inhibitors) for the FDA, Dr. Irving Kirsch concluded: "People may be better off exploring other treatment options. . . . That is much better than the loss of sexual function, tremors, agitation, diarrhea, and nausea that are side effects of SSRIs."[34]

One family physician stated: "After fifteen years of treating depressed patients with pharmacologic agents, it is evident to me that this treatment never cured the true cause of their depression. In fact, I believe it complicated or prolonged a true resolution.

"I have come to the conclusion that, if sought out thoroughly, the root cause of depression, with rare exception, will lie in the unresolved conflicts of the soul."

How to Replace Guilt With Inward Peace

Guilt is a function of the spirit.

Guilt is not a function of the mind but a response of the spirit. It is first and foremost a result of a broken relationship with God and the awareness that we have violated the laws that He has indelibly inscribed in our hearts.

For this reason, shock treatments and chemical drugs, which are used to block out memories and guilt, are not only ineffective but compound the damage of the guilt. It is the spirit that needs to be restored, not just the mind. Therefore, David prayed correctly, "Create in me a clean heart, O God; and renew a right spirit within me."[35]

You may be able to convince your mind that what you did was not wrong. However, your spirit will continue to condemn you with guilt, and that guilt will release a cascade of hormonal imbalances that will affect your mind, will, physical health, and emotional well-being.

Most treatments are ineffective.

The disastrous ineffectiveness of trying to treat guilt with antidepressants is being seen in the increase of suicides among those who take them. One would assume that antidepressants would reduce depression. Instead, they often have the opposite effect.

A large study shows that children who take such drugs have about a 50 percent higher risk of suicidal thoughts and suicide attempts than those who take placebos. This study was conducted by Robert Temple, Director of the Office of Drug Evaluation at the Food and Drug Administration.[36]

The epidemic of suicides from depression.

As the nation has watched the casualty rate on the battlefield, an even higher death rate has surfaced among returning soldiers.

A study conducted by CBS News uncovered the startling fact that in 2005 there were 6,256 suicides among armed forces veterans. That is 120 suicides every week in just one year—more than all the fatalities from the war against terror in Iraq.[37]

These staggering facts should motivate us to identify the real causes of depression and follow practical, proven steps to resolve them. We have a Biblical mandate to do this.

> "If thou forbear to deliver them that are drawn unto death, and those that are ready to be slain; If thou sayest, Behold, we knew it not; doth not he that pondereth the heart consider it? and he that keepeth thy soul, doth not he know it? and shall not he render to every man according to his works?"[38]

It is estimated that one-third of returning soldiers suffer from emotional problems. Many are given antidepressants. In 2005, more than six thousand veterans committed suicide.[39]

Dryness in the desert is like guilt in the bones.

"When I kept silence, my bones waxed old through my roaring all the day long. For day and night thy hand was heavy upon me: my moisture is turned into the drought of summer."[40]

Seven Commands to Conquer Guilt

1. Be Born Again

**"Marvel not that I said unto thee,
Ye must be born again."[41]**

Resulting Quality: Security

Based on the fact that your real person is your spirit and that you were a physical part of Adam when he sinned, you died with Adam. "For as in Adam all die."[42] Therefore, you were born into the world spiritually dead. The only way to become alive is to be born again.

The new birth is a supernatural act of God that is carried out within us by the power of the Holy Spirit when we confess with our mouths that Jesus Christ is our Lord and believe in our hearts that God raised Him from the dead. "For with the heart man believeth unto righteousness; and with the mouth confession is made unto salvation. For the Scripture saith, Whosoever believeth on him shall not be ashamed."[43]

The snake symbolized Christ.

When the nation of Israel turned against God, He sent poisonous snakes among them. Only then did they repent and plead for healing. God told Moses to make a brass snake and nail it to a pole. He commanded all who were bitten to go outside the camp and look at the snake. Only those who followed this instruction were healed.[44]

In the same way, we are to put our faith in the finished work of the Lord Jesus Christ on the cross and receive Him as our personal Lord and Savior. When we receive Him, we are born again.

Personal Application

- ☐ Do I believe that salvation is something I must work for or that it is a gift freely given? If I believe that I must work to earn salvation, I do not understand the new birth. It is a free gift, paid for by the blood of Christ for all who receive Him as their personal Savior.
- ☐ Can I identify a specific time when I was spiritually born again, just as I can state the time and place in which I was physically born?
- ☐ When I received the gift of salvation, did I pray with my voice and heart or did I pray silently?

A symbol of medicine is the caduceus—a snake wrapped around a staff. It can remind us of our need to be born again.

Courtesy of www.SolveFamilyProblems.com

To explain the new birth to Nicodemus, Jesus reminded him of the time when Moses lifted a brass serpent onto a pole.[45]

Our new birth is like a planted seed that, with water and sunshine, will sprout and grow into a fruitful tree.[46]

2. Love the Lord

"Love the Lord thy God with all thy heart, and with all thy soul, and with all thy mind."[47]

Resulting Quality: Enthusiasm

If you were to ask all believers, "Do you love the Lord?" most would say yes. However, a person's idea of love may be entirely different from what God defines as love. God said of the children of Israel, "This people draweth nigh unto me with their mouth, and honoreth me with their lips; but their heart is far from me."[48]

Do not tolerate competing affections.

Salvation is a blood covenant. God compares it to marriage, which also is a blood covenant. In a covenant relationship, there can be no toleration of any competing affection.

One day, an earnest husband was trying to convince his wife that he loved her. He recounted all the things he did to prove his love. It was an impressive list. She responded, "Yes, you do all these things, but I can tell that you do not love me, because when a certain woman walks into the room, your eyes light up for her, and they don't light up like that for me."

The Lord is equally jealous over our total love and loyalty. Thus He states: "Ye adulterers and adulteresses, know ye not that the friendship of the world is enmity with God? whosoever therefore will be a friend of the world is the enemy of God. Do ye think that the Scripture saith in vain, The spirit that dwelleth in us lusteth to envy?"[49]

Do you pass God's test of genuine love?

Jesus tested Peter's love by asking him three times, "Lovest thou me more than these?" After each time Peter answered, Jesus replied, "Feed my lambs" or "Feed my sheep."[50] Only as we lead others to Christ and disciple them with His commands will we see a reason to reject the world and establish high personal standards. We should do nothing that would weaken disciples or cause them to stumble or take offense.

Personal Application

- ☐ If I were to rate my love for Jesus on a scale of 1–10, what number would I select? (10 being the strongest)
- ☐ What competing affections stand between my number and 10?
- ☐ Do I want to love the Lord with all my heart, soul, mind, and strength?
- ☐ Will I now confess and renounce all competing affections and confess secret sins to those to whom I am accountable?

God compares our relationship with Him to that of a marriage—a lifelong covenant.

When an attractive woman walks into a room, a wife will tend to check the eyes of her husband to see if he delights in her. If he does, she will be grieved.

Courtesy of www.SolveFamilyProblems.com

There are three kinds of love that can motivate us.

- ***Agapē*—Divine love**
- ***Phileō*—Friendly affection**
- ***Eros*—Sensual desire**

Jesus demonstrated His love for us by setting aside all His personal riches and laying down His life for us.[51]

3. Hear God's Voice

"He that hath ears to hear, let him hear."[52]

Resulting Quality: Attentiveness

Guilt will not only stop us from hearing God's voice; it will also cause us to misinterpret what He wants to say to us. The cares of this world further choke out the Word of God and the fruit we bear as we apply it to our lives.

"Listen" for the logos *and* rhema *of God's voice.*

"All Scripture is given by inspiration of God."[53] There are two Greek words that describe the Word of God. The first is *logos,* which includes the entire Bible. The second is *rhema,* which involves specific application of the *logos.* As you read through the Bible, the Holy Spirit, Who inspired Scripture, will illuminate your mind with specific verses that He wants you to apply. These are vital for direction and daily victory.

Jesus defeated Satan with rhemas and emphasized their importance when He said, "It is written, That man shall not live by bread alone, but by every word [*rhema*] of God."[54] Scripture states that "The sword of the Spirit is . . . the word [*rhema*] of God."[55] Thus the sword of the Spirit does not necessarily include the whole Bible but the insights and applications God has given you.

All the commands of Christ are rhemas. Thus Jesus said, "If ye abide in me, and my words [*rhema*] abide in you, ye shall ask what ye will [based on these rhemas], and it shall be done unto you."[56]

When God gives you a rhema, He confirms it with one or two more rhemas "that in the mouth of two or three witnesses every word [*rhema*] may be established."[57]

Recognize the "messengers" of God's voice.

Hearing God's voice requires that you recognize the messengers through which His voice comes. First and foremost are the Scriptures. Then there is the Biblical instruction of parents,[58] the wise teaching of pastors,[59] the God-ordained circumstances in our lives,[60] and even dreams.[61]

Personal Application

- ☐ **Do I have any sin in my life that is blocking out God's voice?[62]**
- ☐ **Each morning, God waits to talk to me from His Word. How often am I there to read His Word and hear His voice?[63]**
- ☐ **How much Scripture have I memorized so that God can speak to me throughout the day by bringing it to my mind?**
- ☐ **Have I applied the rhemas He has already given me, recognizing that light received brings more light but light rejected brings darkness?**

God communicates to our spirits with His Spirit. If our lives are under the control of our intellects, we will not hear God's voice.

Many believers do not hear God's voice because they have exalted their intellects, desiring to understand before they obey. The results are fears and doubts about God and the Bible.

A decisive, verbal declaration from our mouths and hearts is necessary to take our intellects off the throne and place them under the authority of God's Word and the Holy Spirit's control.

If we try to do this with silent prayer from our intellects, nothing will happen, because our intellects do not surrender easily.

"For years I doubted my salvation, but when I 'dethroned my intellect,' the doubt and fears went away." —Stephen Baehr

4. Observe Communion

"Jesus took bread . . . and said, Take, eat; this is my body. And he took the cup . . . saying, Drink ye all of it."[64]

Resulting Quality: Thoroughness

God established communion as a regular time to remember His death. It is also a time to thoroughly examine our lives for any hidden sins that would cause guilt in us and bring damage to other members of the Body of Christ. "But let a man examine himself, and so let him eat of that bread, and drink of that cup."[65]

Distinguish the Lord's Table from communion.

The Lord's Table involves an entire meal. Communion includes only the bread and the cup.[66] The Lord's Table originated in the homes of Israelites in Egypt with the Passover lamb.[67] It was established by Jesus in the upper room of a home,[68] it was observed in a home by Jesus with two disciples on the road to Emmaus,[69] and it was practiced by early believers in their homes.[70]

When Corinthian believers tried to bring the Lord's Table into the church along with the bread and the cup, it resulted in confusion. Thus Paul declared: "When ye come together therefore into one place, this is not to eat the Lord's supper. . . . Have ye not houses to eat and to drink in?"[71] Only the bread and the cup should be celebrated in the church after thoroughly clearing up all causes of guilt. Failure to do this will cause weakness, sickness, and premature death.

Jesus did not specify the frequency of communion, nor did He specifically restrict it to one location. It should be observed as often as needed. Furthermore, there are sound Biblical and practical reasons to hold communion in believers' homes as well as in the church.

If conflicts and hurts are not cleared up in homes and family members go to bed angry, Satan will be given jurisdiction in their souls, and they will not be able to properly observe communion at church.[72]

Personal Application

- ☐ **Do I thoroughly examine my life before taking communion?**
- ☐ **Do I realize that if I do not clear up all offenses toward God and others, I could experience weakness, sickness, and premature death?**
- ☐ **Is my goal in communion to remember the Lord's excruciating death for me so that I can live a victorious and fruitful life for Him?**
- ☐ **Have I considered the importance of having communion in my home so that my family and I can maintain the power of one accord?**

Jesus said, "I stand at the door, and knock."[73]

Most of us have assumed that this verse pictures Jesus standing at the door of a nonbeliever's heart. No doubt, this concept has helped many receive Christ.

However, this passage was not written to nonbelievers but to lukewarm Christians. It is more accurate to picture Jesus standing at the door of your home.

In Bible times, the door of a home was the place of covenant making, just as the gate of a city was the place of official business.

Blood was thus placed on the doorposts in Egypt to establish a covenant for the protection of the firstborn sons.

Jesus is knocking at the door in order to come in and have a meal. What better meal to invite Him to than the Lord's Table? We can be sure that Jesus will join us at the meal because He promises, "Where two or three are gathered together in my name, there am I in the midst of them."[74]

"A father establishes his priestly role when he serves communion to his family."

—Dr. Karl Coke

There is no sin known to man that the human mind cannot rationalize away.

I allowed wrong choices to draw me away from God and my parents. These included wrong friends and wrong activities. Then my parents signed me up for a Journey to the Heart.

Down deep, I always wanted to enjoy the presence of God, but I realized that for this to happen, all my "baggage" needed to go.

As my team prayed, I began to cry. Then my team leader talked to me privately, and I was able to open up my heart to her.

I called my parents and confessed everything to them. They forgave me, and I was set free!

When I returned home, I asked all the people I had offended to forgive me. I now have a joy in the Lord that I never thought possible. One statement really changed me:

"The strength of sin is in its secrecy."

—Testimony of Elizabeth Zellon

5. Be Reconciled

"If . . . thou . . . rememberest that thy brother hath aught against thee . . . first be reconciled to thy brother."[75]

Resulting Quality: **Responsibility**

Guilt is the result of broken relationships. Restoring broken relationships is God's priority and should be ours as well. He took the initiative to send His Son into the world to restore our broken relationship with Him. Now He wants us to take the initiative to restore any relationships we have broken by offending Him or others.

Remove barriers to reconciliation.

Most of us can think of many reasons not to ask forgiveness for our faults. Among the first is forgetting who you offended and how you offended them. However, if you go before God and ask Him to remind you of your offenses, He will certainly do it.[76] Another barrier is realizing that you are partly wrong but that the other person is mostly wrong. In this case, you must focus on your offense and leave the rest to God.

A further barrier is not knowing how to contact the one you offended. A face-to-face meeting is best. In some cases, a phone call would be more appropriate. A letter should be avoided because it does not allow for verbal forgiveness. Also, the goal is to erase the past, not document it.

If the person you offended moves away and you have no way to contact him, you should prepare what you are going to say and expect God to bring him across your path.

Have the right attitude.

When you ask someone to forgive you, he will discern whether you are really broken and contrite over your offenses or whether you just want to clear your conscience for your own peace of mind. God describes the attitude you must have: "Be afflicted, and mourn, and weep: let your laughter be turned to mourning, and your joy to heaviness. Humble yourselves in the sight of the Lord, and he shall lift you up."[77]

Personal Application

- ☐ Can I look every person in the eye and know that none can say, "You offended me and never tried to make it right?"
- ☐ How many people stand between me and a conscience void of offense toward God and others?[78] Have I made a list of them?
- ☐ Have I relived my offenses through their feelings so that I can understand how deeply they were hurt by what I did?
- ☐ If a person does not want to forgive me, will I try to resolve the reason or just commit them to God for His timing of reconciliation?

6. Judge Not

"Judge not, that ye be not judged."[79]

Resulting Quality: Discernment

A judgmental attitude toward other people is a sign of guilt. It affirms that we are guilty of the very same things for which we judge other people. God confirms this: "Therefore thou art inexcusable, O man, whosoever thou art that judgest: for wherein thou judgest another, thou condemnest thyself; for thou that judgest doest the same things."[80]

Judging exposes our guilt.

James warns: "Speak not evil one of another, brethren. He that speaketh evil of his brother, and judgeth his brother, speaketh evil of the law, and judgeth the law: but if thou judge the law, thou art not a doer of the law, but a judge. There is one lawgiver, who is able to save and to destroy: who art thou that judgest another?"[81]

What is the relationship between the Law and judging a brother for doing or saying wrong things? The whole Law hangs on two commands: love God and love one another.[82] This verse is basically saying, "The one you are judging acted without love, and you are acting apart from love by judging him." On this basis, both parties are guilty of violating the greatest commandment. There can be no greater sin against God or others than this. Therefore, anything else that is judged is insignificant.

Differentiate discernment from judgment.

There is an important distinction between judging a person for his actions and discerning the moral nature of a matter. The Greek word translated *judge* in this command is *krinō*. It means "to pass sentence, to give one's opinion in a private manner, to condemn."[83]

Discern comes from the Greek word *diakrinō*, which means "to make a distinction on a moral issue."[84] We are told in Scripture that maturity in the Christian life is based on our ability to "Discern between good and evil."[85] In order to give counsel, we must first discern the nature of the problem.

Personal Application

- ☐ **Who irritates me and causes me to judge them?**
- ☐ **Do I have a genuine love for these people, or have I despised them and cut them off in my spirit?**
- ☐ **Do I have similar problems in my life that make me sensitive to their needs, and do I have an answer based on how I solved my problem?**
- ☐ **Have I earned the right to talk to them about the problem they are having and the solutions I have experienced?**

God has established judges to carefully weigh all the evidence and give rulings. When we judge, we usurp God-given authority. Our job is not to condemn but to "reprove, rebuke, exhort with all longsuffering and doctrine."[86]

God calls every believer to discern between good and evil and to help those who have chosen to do evil to see the error of their way.

Courtesy of www.SolveFamilyProblems.com

Judging produces severe harshness in those who do it.

David went beyond the Law when he condemned the rich man to death for simply stealing a pet lamb, because he was guilty of doing that very thing.[87]

The Pharisees had an elaborate system of swearing by things of differing importance. The more important the item, the more likely they were to keep their promises.

The Basic Seminar, which has attracted so many youth and adults to God's way of life, is actually the result of catching up on a vow of talking to at least three people a day about the Lord. This required seeking out groups of teens, including Chicago street gangs. From the results, non-optional principles of life were identified.

7. Keep Your Word

"Let your communication be, Yea, yea; Nay, nay: for whatsoever is more than these cometh of evil."[88]

Resulting Quality: **Truthfulness**

One of the deepest sources of guilt is unfulfilled promises we have made to other people. For this reason, God warns us not to make hasty decisions. "For by thy words thou shalt be justified, and by thy words thou shalt be condemned."[89]

Unwise financial agreements are particularly grievous. Therefore, God warns: "My son, if thou be surety for thy friend, if thou hast stricken thy hand with a stranger, Thou art snared with the words of thy mouth, thou art taken with the words of thy mouth."[90]

Discover the starting point for truthfulness.

The most important promises to keep are promises made to God. If you have been in a crisis, and you told Him that if He delivered you, you would do something for Him, you must go back and carry out what you promised—unless it was a foolish vow or a promise that you would exceed your jurisdiction in carrying out.

"When thou vowest a vow unto God, defer not to pay it; for he hath no pleasure in fools: pay that which thou hast vowed. . . . Neither say thou before the angel, that it was an error: wherefore should God be angry at thy voice, and destroy the work of thine hands?"[91]

One of the most practical (and painful) ways to carry out this command is to get a sheet of blank paper and ask those around you if you have ever made promises to them that you have not yet carried out. You will probably be surprised at what they remember and what you have forgotten!

Some may require sacrifice, but God encourages us to fulfill them. In Psalm 15, He promises that we will never fall if we do eleven things. One is to fulfill promises that require more sacrifice than we planned: "He that sweareth to his own hurt, and changeth not."[92]

Personal Application

- ☐ What vows or promises have I made to God that I have not been faithful in fulfilling? What can I do now to carry them out?
- ☐ What promises have I made to other people that I have not kept? How can I fulfill each of these?
- ☐ Have I taken a sheet of paper and written down unfulfilled promises?
- ☐ What "guards" can I put at my lips so that I will not make unwise promises or vows?

Lust

How we deny or reveal lust

"I am not lustful . . ."	Ways we reveal lust
"I am only admiring beauty."	A second look for pleasure
"God made me this way."	Dressing to attract attention
"It doesn't hurt anyone."	Looking at pornography
"It's not wrong to look."	Sensual behavior
"I just have a crush."	A love/hate response
"I can't control my desires."	Being overly friendly
"I wish I were married."	Flattering others
"Life is for pleasure."	Inappropriate touching
"God wants me happy."	Fantasizing and daydreaming
"It does not affect me."	Inability to concentrate

How to Resolve

Lust

Required Command	Resulting Quality
Honor God's Law Matthew 5:17	**Love** vs. Selfishness
Do Not Lust Matthew 5:28–30	**Self-Control** vs. Self-Indulgence
Practice Disciplines Matthew 6:1–18	**Faith** vs. Unbelief
Choose the Narrow Way Matthew 7:13–14	**Decisiveness** vs. Double-Mindedness
Reject False Prophets Matthew 7:15–16	**Alertness** vs. Carelessness
Beware of Leaven Matthew 16:6	**Virtue** vs. Weakness
Honor Marriage Matthew 19:4–6	**Loyalty** vs. Infidelity

13

How Does Lust Affect the Endocrine System?

The endocrine system is composed of sixteen endocrine glands located in different parts of the body. These secrete hormones that regulate and maintain balance within the body (homeostasis).

Hormones are chemical messengers that are formed in one tissue and released to influence another tissue or organ. The word *hormone* comes from the Greek root *hormōn*, which means "to urge on."[1]

Many hormones directly and indirectly influence the production of other hormones. Some have specific target tissues, while others have widespread effects.

For example, insulin is a hormone that is necessary for the proper functioning of every tissue in the body except the nerve cells.[2]

Hormones play a key role in the regulation of all bodily functions, including metabolism, growth and development, water and electrolyte balance, reproduction, and behavior.[3]

Statistics of Related Diseases

In this day of sexual promiscuity, we have a resulting pandemic of sex-related diseases. These include infectious and incurable viruses such as HIV, hepatitis B, HPV, and related cancers. There are also infectious bacterial diseases such as chlamydia, gonorrhea, and syphilis.

The estimated number of people living in the United States with a viral sexually transmitted disease (STD) and/or sexually transmitted infection (STI) is more than 65 million.

Every year, there are at least 19 million new cases of STDs/STIs.[4,5] A few of them are treatable medically, but the mental, emotional, and spiritual damage continues to bring destruction. As promised by God, "He that soweth to his flesh shall of the flesh reap corruption."[6] Each year, one in four teenagers contracts an STD/STI.[7]

How Lust Relates to Anger

Lust and anger are "twins." A person who is angry will usually have lust, and one who has lust will usually have anger as well.

There is a medical connection that explains this relationship. In the central nervous system (CNS), there is a reward center associated with the lateral nucleus. If this is lightly stimulated, it will produce

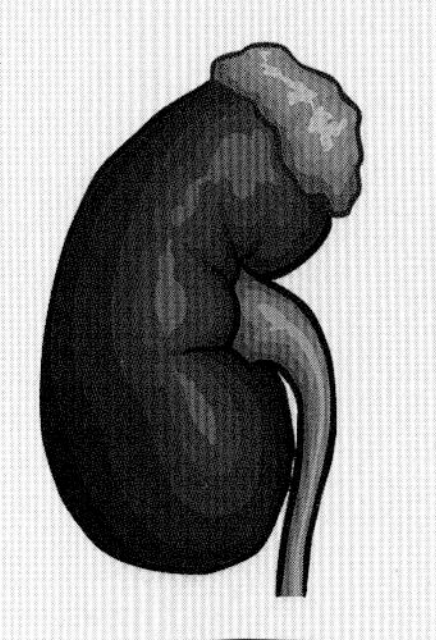

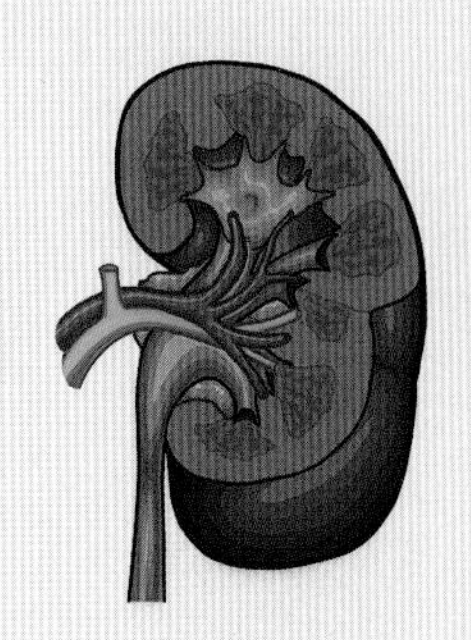

The kidneys are among sixteen organs that make up the endocrine system. They are responsible to maintain hormonal balance in the body.[8]

New drugs that treat impotency are being bought by millions of men who then experience serious side effects.[9] A root cause is lust, which creates imbalance.

The end result of lust and associated guilt will produce an imbalance in the parasympathetic nervous system, which inhibits a man from having fulfilling physical consummation in marriage. Lust can affect a woman's ability to reproduce due to imbalances in her central nervous system. The CNS controls the release of hormones that are necessary for ovulation.[10]

Lust originated in the Garden of Eden. The tree of the knowledge of good and evil had fruit that was pleasant to the eye and "to be desired" (lusted after).[19]

Adam and Eve had no comprehension of the far-reaching devastation that would result from that one act of momentary pleasure.[20]

All eating disorders have their roots in the Garden of Eden. The chief cause is taking control of our own decisions about what we eat and drink and what we do not eat and drink.

a sense of well-being and fulfillment. However, if it is overstimulated, it produces rage.[11]

A Hebrew word for *lust* is *châmad,* which means "to desire, to covet, to long for, to be desired, to feel delight."[12] This word is used in the description of the forbidden tree in the Garden of Eden[13] and in the command not to covet.[14] Lust refers to an inordinate, ungoverned, selfish desire. Such uncontrolled passion can be expressed in either lust or anger.

A Stunning Warning

Just as Adam and Eve had no comprehension of the far-reaching consequences of their surrender to lust and covetousness, so people today have no understanding of the deep and devastating destruction that results from the effects of lust. Therefore, Jesus gives a shocking comparison.

He explains that it would be more profitable for a man to rip out his right eye and chop off his right hand than to secretly lust after a women in his heart.[15]

These barbaric actions are unthinkable and should not be carried out, because they would not solve the problem of lust.

Lust does not originate with the sight of the eye or the action of the hand but with the thoughts of the heart. Only as a person changes the belief system of his heart will he be able to control the lust of the eyes and the flesh.

Jesus is not telling us to pluck out our eyes or cut off our hands. He is saying that if we want to understand the seriousness of what we think is a "harmless pleasure," we had better think again.

The Lust of the Flesh

Even after being born again and experiencing the Holy Spirit within your spirit, you will have a raging battlefield in your soul and flesh.

On the one hand, your mind will want to do what is right, and on the other hand, the law of sin in your flesh will overpower the law of your mind, and you will do evil.

Paul describes this lust of the flesh: "When we were in the flesh [living according to the dictates of our fleshly desires], the motions [passions] of sins . . . did work in our members to bring forth fruit unto death. . . . For I know that in me (that is, in my flesh,) dwelleth no good thing."[16]

Notwithstanding this fierce battle, believers have the confidence that if we follow God's commands, we will experience victory over the flesh, according to the promise of Scripture.

"Let not sin therefore reign in your mortal body, that ye should obey it in the lusts thereof. Neither yield ye your members as instruments of unrighteousness unto sin: but yield yourselves unto God, as those that are alive from the dead, and your members as instruments of righteousness unto God. For sin shall not have dominion over you: for ye are not under the law, but under grace."[17]

The Cause of Obesity

The stress of uncontrolled desires can manifest itself in an increased appetite due to elevated levels of stress hormones such as cortisol.[18] This can lead to excessive weight gain and obesity, which is now a national epidemic in

America and a leading cause of diabetes.[21,22,23]

Currently, an estimated 65% of American adults are either overweight or obese.[24] We used to think that fat cells were simply storage containers for toxins in the body. Now we understand that they actually act as endocrine organs that secrete hormones and inflammatory mediators.[25,26]

One such hormone, leptin, sends a signal to the brain to slow down food intake. However, if elevated levels of this hormone are sustained, the body will become insensitive to it in the same way that the body becomes resistant to insulin in type 2 diabetes.[27,28]

The Connection Between Food and Lust

The connection between food and lust is clearly established in Scripture. Adam and Eve's transgression in the garden began with a desire for forbidden food.[29] Cain's argument with his brother was over an offering of food.[30]

While Moses was on Mount Sinai, the Israelites sat down to eat and drink and rose up for sexual play. The head of John the Baptist was cut off because Herod sat down to a feast and was lured into a wrong decision by the sensual dancing of Salome.[31]

In the days of Noah, people focused on food and marriages that violated God's design. This will be the case again at the time of Christ's return.[32]

The Lust of the Mind

Scripture makes a distinction between the lust of the flesh and the lust of the mind. Paul wrote, "We all had our conversation [way of life] in times past in the *lusts* of our *flesh,* fulfilling the desires of the *flesh* and of the *mind;* and were by nature the children of wrath, even as others."[33]

The Greek word for *mind* is *dianoia.* It refers to the intellect of the soul. We are warned to "abstain from fleshly lusts, which war against the soul."[34]

The lustful thoughts and desires of the mind strengthen and reinforce the lusts of the flesh and bring about the destruction of sin: "Every man is tempted, when he is drawn away of his own lust, and enticed. Then when lust hath conceived, it bringeth forth sin: and sin, when it is finished, bringeth forth death."[35]

The mind is subject to lustful thoughts that come from the things we see, hear, and do. Thoughts can originate from our own reasoning, from other people, or from Satan himself. This was the case when Peter told Jesus that He would not die.[36]

Therefore, the mind must be viewed as a battlefield of not just the thoughts and ideas of the soul but also of the heart. We must take each thought captive until it is in harmony with the truth of Christ's teaching.

"The weapons of our warfare are not carnal, but mighty through God to the pulling down of strongholds . . . Casting down imaginations, and every high thing that exalteth itself against the knowledge of God, and bringing into captivity every thought to the obedience of Christ."[37]

The Lust of the Heart

When the lust of a person's flesh or mind becomes the lust of

Courtesy of www.SolveFamilyProblems.com

The rampant indulgence of immorality, gluttony, and drunkenness in the days of Noah will be repeated before Christ returns.

Today's technology can be a frightful means for this corruption, leading to "every imagination of the thoughts" being "only evil continually."[38]

"As the days of Noah were, so shall also the coming of the Son of man be."[39]

The rainbow is the sign of God's covenant that He will not destroy the earth with another flood.

However, He will discipline those who violate His moral laws with weakness, sickness, and disease in hopes that they will seek His forgiveness and serve Him with a pure spirit and a transformed soul.

Louis Pasteur operated on the assumption that germs cause infection. But later he concluded that germs do not cause infection.[54] They are simply scavengers that feed on toxins in the body.

The stress of immorality breaks down healthy tissue and provides the toxins that germs need to thrive on.

A continual war takes place in our bodies. Cancer cells develop every day, but they are quickly destroyed by a strong immune system.

Deep, secret hurts from immorality weaken the immune system, allowing cancer cells to multiply.[55,56]

his heart, he is in serious trouble. We can deal with temptations of the flesh and mind, but we are what we believe in our hearts: "For as he thinketh in his heart, so is he."[40] "For out of the heart proceed evil thoughts, murders, adulteries, fornications . . . These are the things which defile a man."[41]

When God saw that the imaginations of the hearts of men were continually wicked, He sent the Flood.[42]

The heart is the central control system of a person's entire being. It is, then, no wonder that God wants us to guard the heart "with all diligence; for out of it are the issues of life."[43] This is why Jesus' warning was so severe about lusting after a woman in our hearts.

Conquering Lust

God has given clear instruction on how to deal with lust on three different levels. He has also given precise warnings on what will happen to those who fail to resolve the stress of lust.

1. The Lust of the Flesh

The flesh is not meant to be a master but a servant. Paul explains that the body was not designed for the momentary sensual pleasures of fornication "but for the Lord; and the Lord for the body."[44] Therefore, he appeals to everyone to present his body to God as a "living sacrifice" in a definite act of worship.[45] Thereafter, we are to yield the members of our bodies to Him as instruments of righteousness.[46]

Paul was aware of the ever-present tendency to surrender to the lust of the flesh and thus lose the great potential that he had to win the prize in his race: "But I keep under my body, and bring it into subjection: lest that by any means, when I have preached to others, I myself should be a castaway."[47]

If, on the other hand, we fail to develop and maintain these inward disciplines, choosing instead to indulge in the lust of the flesh, we will experience corresponding physical weakness, disease, and death, "For he that soweth to his flesh shall of the flesh reap corruption; but he that soweth to the Spirit shall of the Spirit reap life everlasting."[48]

The Book of Proverbs gives a description of a simple young man who is approached by a lewd, immoral woman. With her sensual dress, smooth talk, and alluring reasoning, she convinced him to follow her to her house.

"He goeth after her straightway, as an ox goeth to the slaughter, or as a fool to the correction of the stocks; Till a dart strike through his liver."[49]

The medical connection between immoral behavior and damage to the liver is clearly established. The primary transmission of hepatitis B and C (infections of the liver) is through sexual promiscuity.[50,51]

God associates immoral women with drinking, which also harms the liver.[52] Alcohol is toxic to the liver, and a leading cause of liver cirrhosis in the United States is alcohol abuse.[53]

2. The Lust of the Mind

If we fill our minds with God's Word, especially the commands of Christ, we will not only clean out impure thoughts, but we will send to our hearts the truths through which a belief system can be built.

From this belief system, we will be able to think, speak, and act according to God's ways, thereby conquering moral impurity. The psalmist understood this when he said, "Thy word have I hid in mine heart, that I might not sin against thee."[57]

Jesus told His disciples: "Now ye are clean through the word which I have spoken unto you. . . . If ye abide in me, and my words abide in you, ye shall ask what ye will, and it shall be done unto you."[58]

This would include victory over sensual thoughts. Jesus made this goal a part of his final prayer: "Sanctify them through thy truth: thy word is truth."[59]

If we fail to bring every thought into the captivity of the truth of Christ's words, we will run our lives on our own thoughts, which are opposite to God's truth and life: "For to be carnally minded is death; but to be spiritually minded is life and peace."[60]

Man's thoughts are completely opposite to God's thoughts. If we trust in them, we will experience mental, emotional, physical, and spiritual death. "There is a way that seemeth right unto a man, but the end thereof are the ways of death."[61]

If we reject God's truth, He will turn us over to a reprobate mind, and we will believe a lie.[62] He will send a "strong delusion."[63]

3. The Lust of the Heart

Conquering the lust of the heart is a greater challenge, because we all tend to believe that what we think in our hearts is no one's business but ours. Furthermore, we think that our secret meditations will not hurt us or anyone else. Nothing could be further from the truth.

God warns against this kind of thinking: "Lest there should be among you man, or woman, or family, or tribe, whose heart turneth away this day from the LORD our God, to go and serve the gods of these nations; lest there should be among you a root that beareth gall and wormwood; And it come to pass, when he heareth the words of this curse, that he bless himself in his heart, saying, I shall have peace, though I walk in the imagination of mine heart, to add drunkenness to thirst."[64]

The phrase in this passage about "a root that beareth gall and wormwood" is very significant. It is further explained in Hebrews 12:15: "Be careful that none of you fails to respond to the grace which God gives, for if he does there can very easily spring up in him a bitter spirit which is not only bad in itself but can also poison the lives of many others."[65]

The permeating effect of sensual living is compared in Scripture to a little bit of leaven in a lump of dough. Before long, the little bit of leaven will spread throughout the whole lump.[66] To avoid this, Paul instructed the Corinthian church to turn over an immoral man to Satan "for the destruction of the flesh, that the spirit may be saved in the day of the Lord Jesus."[67]

When the lust of a person's heart is given freedom to express itself in immoral living, God often will give him an incurable disease. This is what He warned about in Deuteronomy 28:21–22a: "The LORD shall make

God uses graphic illustrations to warn a young man to flee immoral women.[68]

They will lead him away like an ox to the slaughter (taking away his life), like a bird into a snare (taking away his freedom), and like a fool to the stocks (taking away his good name and reputation).[69]

The eye that lusts after wine will also lust after immoral women.

"Look not thou upon the wine when it is red . . . . At the last it biteth like a serpent, and stingeth like an adder. Thine eyes shall behold strange women."[70]

The toxic nature of gall and wormwood symbolizes the bitterness that comes from engaging in immoral acts.

Just as a little leaven leavens a whole lump of dough,[73] so a little immorality that a person tolerates in his life will soon corrupt his entire being.

Leaven spreads through a lump of dough at room temperature and quickly permeates the entire lump, causing it to puff up.

the pestilence cleave unto thee, until he have consumed thee . . . . The LORD shall smite thee with a consumption, and with a fever, and with an inflammation, and with an extreme burning."

If God chooses to send an incurable disease to a person who has rejected His moral standards, that person would then be wise to realize that he must primarily deal with God on this matter rather than search for some cure to relieve the symptoms.[71]

How God Healed an "Incurable" Condition

God promises to hear and respond to the sincere cry of those who want freedom from the bondage of lust. Thus He says, "Call upon me in the day of trouble: I will deliver thee, and thou shalt glorify me."[72]

The following account is a powerful illustration of how God uses the pressure of incurable conditions to bring deeper healing to a person's life.

John is a pharmacist in Minnesota. Several years ago, a woman handed him a prescription for a medication to treat a serious eye condition. In filling the prescription, he put together the wrong medication. She went home and applied it to her eyes.

The burning sensation was almost unbearable, so she called her eye doctor and reported what had happened. He assured her that her eyes would get used to it and instructed her to continue to use it.

Each day her eyes reacted more intensely to the medication, even bleeding at times. She then went to see her doctor. When he saw her condition, he was shocked and alarmed. After reading the medication label, he realized that she had been given the wrong prescription.

She went back to John and told him what had happened. He was terrified because he realized that he was legally liable. He assured her that he would do all that he could to help her.

As the weeks passed, her condition grew worse. Finally, John spent a few days alone with the Lord. When he cried out to God for this woman's health, God reminded him of an area of moral impurity in his life.

He surrendered it to the Lord and purposed to tell his wife. The next day, John returned home and called it his D-day, which meant "Death-to-self Day." He poured out his moral failures to his wife. She then informed him that she had been planning to leave him with their three children because she knew that something was wrong but did not know what it was.

However, because he came to her in humility and brokenness, she determined to stay with him. A few days later, the eyes of the patient totally cleared up. John later wrote: "It is only because of God's grace, my wife's forgiveness, and step six of *The Eagle Story* that the Lord has allowed my marriage to remain intact. I am so grateful to God."

Only when John came to total humility and brokenness and cried out to God with all his heart in unconditional surrender was God willing to work.

How to Transform Lust Into the Dynamic of Genuine Love

It is just as impossible to control the lusts of the mind and flesh as it is to control the words of the tongue, which God states that no one can tame. This is the case because both thoughts and words are controlled by the heart. Only as you bring your heart into submission to the control of God's Holy Spirit will you be able to control the lusts of your mind and flesh.

This is accomplished by building a belief system in your heart that is made up of the truth of God's Word. For this reason, the psalmist declared, "Thy word have I hid in mine heart, that I might not sin against thee."[74]

Guard your heart.

We are instructed to guard the heart "with all diligence; for out of it are the issues of life."[75] It is therefore appropriate to picture your heart as a living, thinking organ that has various gates and chambers. Each gate must have a guard watching it.

The sentries of your heart must be the powerful, living rhemas of God. If you have heart guards of precise Scriptures standing at the doors of your heart, you will be able to take captive every thought and temptation.

Jesus demonstrated this response when He was tempted by Satan. For every temptation that Satan used, Jesus had a precise Scripture to quote.[76] He knew the Scripture from memory and was able to skillfully use it in the right way. Thus you also must have specific Scriptures in your heart that you can use for every temptation.

Rebuild the walls and gates.

Another analogy that could apply to the heart is the rebuilding of the walls of Jerusalem in the days of Nehemiah. The enemies of the Lord came in at will and plundered the people because the walls were broken down and the gates were burned. When Nehemiah began his rebuilding program, there was continuous opposition. However, nothing stopped him from securing the city and placing guards at the entrances.[77]

Similarly, you should memorize precise Scriptures in order to challenge and reject every wrong thought that approaches your heart.

1. **Anger** *(Ephesians 4:31–32)*
2. **Guilt** *(I Timothy 1:19)*
3. **Lust** *(Matthew 5:27–32)*
4. **Bitterness** *(Hebrews 12:15)*
5. **Greed** *(I Timothy 6:6–11)*
6. **Fear** *(II Timothy 1:7)*
7. **Envy** *(Proverbs 14:30)*
8. **Pride** *(Proverbs 22:4)*
9. **Discouragement** *(Joshua 1:8)*
10. **Sensual Music** *(Ephesians 5:18–20)*
11. **Worldly Friends** *(Proverbs 13:20)*
12. **Wasting Time** *(Ephesians 5:16)*

For centuries, the city of Constantinople was considered to be invincible because of its strong walls and God-fearing heritage.

On May 29, 1453, their complacency was shattered when enemy invaders discovered an unlocked gate and then poured through it to conquer the city.[78]

All Satan needs is an unguarded moment to destroy a lifetime of potential.

Courtesy of www.SolveFamilyProblems.com

"The law was given by Moses, but grace and truth came by Jesus Christ."[88]

Grace gives us the desire and the power to keep Christ's commands. Therefore, "His commandments are not grievous."[89]

Courtesy of www.SolveFamilyProblems.com

On the road to Emmaus, Jesus explained to two disciples how all the Law and the prophets referred to Him.

Later they said, "Did not our heart burn within us, while he talked with us by the way, and while he opened to us the Scriptures?"[90]

Seven Commands to Conquer Lust

1. Honor God's Law

"Think not that I am come to destroy the law, or the prophets: I am not come to destroy, but to fulfill."[79]

Resulting Quality: Love

Lust thrives when we decide for ourselves what is right and what is wrong. However, our own opinions must change when we honor God's Law. Paul points this out when he writes, "I had not known sin, but by the law: for I had not known lust, except the law had said, Thou shalt not covet."[80] Thus the Law was written in order to establish a universal standard of right and wrong "that every mouth may be stopped, and all the world may become guilty before God."[81]

God has given three law systems.

God has given three different law systems to mankind. The first was given to one couple—Adam and Eve.[82] The second was given to one nation—Israel.[83] The third was given to all nations—the commands of Christ. All three are founded on the great commands of loving God and loving one another.[84]

The laws, statutes, and judgments given to Moses contained exceptions because of the hardness of the Israelites' hearts.[85] However, grace and truth came by Jesus Christ to give us the power to keep His commands. These go to the very heart of every issue, such as the heart attitude of lust, not the act of adultery.[86] Jesus did not send us out to teach the Ten Commandments but rather His commands.[87]

The Law of Moses was fulfilled in Christ.

Jesus completely fulfilled all the demands of the Law of Moses and was therefore able to die in our place. When we become Christians, we enter into Christ and His perfect fulfillment of the Law.

Personal Application

- ☐ Have I put God's Law above my own opinions of right and wrong?
- ☐ Have I read the three law systems that God has given to mankind so that I can understand how to apply them to my life?
- ☐ Do I realize that when I received Jesus as my Savior, I identified with His life, death, and perfect fulfillment of the Law?
- ☐ Am I meditating on the Law of God day and night so that I can experience the prosperity and success that He promises through it?

2. Do Not Lust

"Whosoever looketh on a woman to lust after her hath committed adultery with her already in his heart."[91]

Resulting Quality: Self-Control

Adultery is not just the physical act of sexual immorality. It is the indulgence of that act in the imaginations of the heart: "For out of the heart proceed evil thoughts, murders, adulteries, fornications."[92]

Understand how the heart commits adultery.

Jesus did not equate a man lusting after a woman with simply committing adultery in his heart. Instead, Jesus said that he is committing adultery *with her* in his heart. This may indicate that the lust of his heart has some effect on the one he is lusting after.

This influence could be explained by the fact that the heart is an electrical organ. We know from the research of Dr. Harold Burr and others that the heart has a powerful electrodynamic field around it, which could affect the lives of other people.[93]

Paul explains this phenomenon with a different illustration. He says that we have a distinct effect on the lives of others—an effect they can sense. To believers, we are a savor of life, and to nonbelievers, we are a savor of death.[94]

Recognize the value of a pure heart.

In this command, Jesus is saying that a pure heart is more valuable than the combined value of a right eye and a right hand. He is explaining that if we lust in our hearts, we are going to be destroyed physically, mentally, emotionally, and spiritually.

On the other hand, we will gain God's vision and bless the lives of multitudes if we transfer our sexual energy into spiritual power: "Blessed are the pure in heart: for they shall see God."[95] "He that believeth on me, as the Scripture hath said, out of his belly shall flow rivers of living water."[96]

Personal Application

- ☐ Do I realize that my lust will affect those whom I lust after?
- ☐ Am I aware that lust upsets my hormonal balance, which will decrease my ability for physical fulfillment in marriage?
- ☐ When I am tempted to lust, do I picture the unthinkable act of plucking out my right eye or cutting off my right hand?
- ☐ Have I purposed to transform my sexual energy into dynamic spiritual power through the grace and power of God's Spirit?

Courtesy of www.SolveFamilyProblems.com

When Jesus looked at a woman, he saw past her outward appearance and had compassion on the condition of her heart, her need for protection, her physical infirmities, her fears, and her level of faith.

Everyone who looks at pornography in any form is guilty of heart adultery.

Strong physical drives can be transformed into great spiritual power.

The one who controls our money controls our lives.

The future antichrist will control all money and rule the world.

Elijah had the same passions that we have, but he turned them into spiritual power through his fervent, effectual prayer.

Courtesy of www.SolveFamilyProblems.com

Daniel's success began with a vow not to defile himself and continued with fervent fasting and prayer.[102]

3. Practice Disciplines

"Thy Father which seeth in secret himself shall reward thee openly."[97]

Resulting Quality: Faith

The members of God's "hall of fame" conquered lust by the faith of secret disciplines. "Without faith it is impossible to please him: for he that cometh to God must believe that he is [alive], and that he is a rewarder of them that diligently seek him."[98] Your faith will multiply as you practice the secret disciplines of giving, praying, and fasting.

Build the discipline of giving.

To many, money represents power and security. Moses was in line to be the next Pharaoh, because the people viewed him as a god who was given to them from the Nile River, which they worshiped. "By faith Moses . . . refused to be called the son of Pharaoh's daughter; Choosing rather to suffer affliction with the people of God, than to enjoy the pleasures of sin for a season; Esteeming the reproach of Christ greater riches than the treasures in Egypt."[99]

Cultivate the discipline of praying.

Prayer that conquers lust must go beyond the words of the intellect and become the fervent cry of the heart, because the fervent, effectual prayer of a righteous man makes much power available.[100] Also, when a group of believers cry out with one accord, God promises to deliver them so that they can glorify Him.[101]

Establish the discipline of fasting.

During a fast of between three and forty days, sexual desires diminish and spiritual desires increase. It is significant that there is no mention of Samson, David, or Solomon going through long fasts, and they fell into moral impurity. Scripture records long fasts for Moses, Daniel, and Jesus, all of whom did not fail. Other factors were certainly involved; however, we know that fasting weakens the bondage of lust.

Personal Application

- ☐ Have I transferred the control of all my resources to God, including time, money, and possessions, and demonstrated this by generosity?
- ☐ Have I ever experienced the power that comes from one-accord prayer?
- ☐ How many days have I fasted and prayed for deliverance from lust?
- ☐ What personal vows have I made to abstain from lustful pleasures and carry out Godly disciplines? Have I kept these vows?

4. Choose the Narrow Way

"Narrow is the way, which leadeth unto life, and few there be that find it."[103]

Resulting Quality: Decisiveness

The term *broadway* has come to symbolize all the delusive glamour, worldly entertainment, and lustful pleasures of American culture. Yet this nation was founded by Godly men and women who chose the narrow way. God has blessed their sacrifices, and now we have the responsibility to rediscover the principles that made America great.

Enoch chose the narrow way.

Enoch achieved what no other man did in his day. He walked with God so closely that God translated him into heaven without death.[104] What was his secret?

In Hebrew, the name Enoch is from the root word *chanakh,* which means "to narrow." It implies "to teach, to dedicate, to consecrate."[105] Enoch was a great proclaimer of truth and was the grandfather of Noah. Enoch walked in the light of God's presence. "If we walk in the light, as he is in the light, we have fellowship one with another, and the blood of Jesus Christ his Son cleanseth us from all sin."[106]

Joseph chose the narrow way.

Joseph could have given many excuses for falling into an immoral relationship with Potiphar's wife. He was a purchased slave in a foreign land, his master's wife urged him to do it, he was rejected by his jealous brothers, and the law that forbade adultery had not yet been written.

But Joseph was able to withstand this powerful temptation, because when he was a young boy, God gave him a clear vision of doing great works. That vision gave him the maturity to forgive his brothers and the motivation to reject lust, rejoice in the midst of false accusation, and withstand harsh prison life.

When you realize that God created you for great works and you dedicate your life to achieving them, you can then view life as a race against time and see the narrow way as the track to keep on the path to victory.

Personal Application

- ☐ **Do I have a purpose in life that is worth living and dying for?**
- ☐ **Have I purposed to make my life count for God by looking at it as a race against time and laying aside every weight and sin?**
- ☐ **Have I accepted higher standards for my life so that I can win the prize?**
- ☐ **Regarding worldly pleasures, have I embraced the joyful motto "others may, but I cannot?"**

The narrow way is not a restriction of freedom but a protection for success.

The narrow track of a runner keeps him on course to win the prize.

The closer we come to Christ, the brighter His light will shine and the narrower our path will be.

"But the path of the just is as the shining light, that shineth more and more unto the perfect day."[107]

Courtesy of www.SolveFamilyProblems.com

Joseph conquered lust by seeing it as a sin against God, not just Potiphar's wife.

"How then can I do this great wickedness, and sin against God?"[108]

Truth out of balance leads to heresy.

For every truth, God gives a balancing truth. Examples: labor and rest, prayer and work, grace to do God's will and mercy when we fail.

Those who refuse to be accountable to their Creator find it convenient to disregard scientific data and accept the preposterous theory of evolution.

Removing God's power from His grace turns grace into a license to sin.

"For there are certain men crept in unawares . . . ungodly men, turning the grace of our God into lasciviousness."[114]

5. Reject False Prophets

"Beware of false prophets . . . they are ravening wolves."[109]

Resulting Quality: Alertness

False prophets exploit lustful people. They promise pleasures and challenge long-held standards of Godly living. Peter describes them as those who "bring in damnable heresies . . . . And many shall follow their pernicious [lustful] ways; by reason of whom the way of truth shall be evil spoken of. . . . Having eyes full of adultery, and that cannot cease from sin; beguiling unstable souls: a heart they have exercised with covetous practices; cursed children . . . . While they promise them liberty, they themselves are the servants of corruption: for of whom a man is overcome, of the same is he brought in bondage."[110]

Identify truth out of balance.

Truth out of balance will always lead to heresy. A prime example is the foundational truth of God's grace. The truth is that grace is God's unmerited favor, which He freely gives to all people. The imbalance is denying that God's grace has the power that we need to carry out Christ's commands and experience victory over lust and other sins.[111]

Those who claim that the grace of God has no inherent power but is simply an attitude of God toward a sinner turn God's grace from the power for doing good into a license to do evil.

Experience the power of God's grace.

The word *grace* appears 122 times in the New Testament. All of these passages can be divided into nine categories. Each one explains a distinct aspect of the power of God's grace.[112] One of these explains the power to serve God: "By the grace of God I am what I am: and his grace which was bestowed upon me was not in vain; but I labored more abundantly than they all: yet not I, but the grace of God which was with me."[113]

Personal Application

- ☐ Do I realize that lust in my heart will make me vulnerable to false prophets who will explain away any guilt I have for my sin?
- ☐ Will I search out every teaching to make sure that it conforms to the whole counsel of God?
- ☐ Do I believe that God's grace is not only unmerited favor but also the desire and power to do His will?
- ☐ Will I ask God each day to multiply His grace to me so that I can understand and live out all His commands?

6. Beware of Leaven

"Beware ye of the leaven of the Pharisees, which is hypocrisy."[115]

Resulting Quality: **Virtue**

There is a strong analogy between lust and leaven. If we allow a little sensuality into our lives or our church fellowships, it will soon permeate our whole lives and the entire Church Body.

Paul uses this very analogy in his instruction to carry out discipline in the Corinthian church. They had allowed one man who was living in sexual immorality to be in their fellowship. Paul writes: "Know ye not that a little leaven leaveneth the whole lump? Purge out therefore the old leaven, that ye may be a new lump, as ye are unleavened."[116]

Leaven spreads rapidly throughout a lump of dough at room temperature, which is lukewarm. When heat is then applied, it puffs up. Paul notes this condition in the Corinthian believers: "Ye are puffed up, and have not rather mourned, that he that hath done this deed might be taken away from among you."[117] Paul further identifies this condition as a symptom of a lack of genuine love: "Charity . . . is not puffed up."[118]

What is the "doctrine of the Pharisees"?

The leaven in this command refers to the "doctrine of the Pharisees and of the Sadducees."[119] Jesus illustrated the hypocrisy of their doctrine as it related to the command to honor parents. They gave lip service to the command. However, they added their own traditions, which actually voided it.

"Thus have ye made the commandment of God of none effect by your tradition. Ye hypocrites, well did Isaiah prophesy of you, saying, This people draweth nigh unto me with their mouth, and honoreth me with their lips; but their heart is far from me. But in vain they do worship me, teaching for doctrines the commandments of men."[120]

A prime example of this in our day is the teaching that when sons and daughters reach legal age, they no longer need to seek their parents' blessing for marriage.

Personal Application

- ☐ Do I have a close friendship with anyone who is immoral?
- ☐ Do I allow lustful activities and excuse them as "just little things?"
- ☐ Have I purposed to live by Christ's commands and not allow contemporary traditions to make them void?
- ☐ Do I realize that marrying someone without the blessing of both sets of parents is publically dishonoring my parents?

A surprising number of inmates in the California juvenile prison system have participated in church worship teams. They used this involvement as an opportunity to defile many young ladies.[121]

This tragedy occurs because of the lack of discernment in church leaders who are more focused on patronizing the lost than equipping the saints.

We require a couple to vow before God and witnesses that they will stay married "till death do us part." Then we encourage divorce and remarriage when we decide that the marriage is not working out!

"Thus have ye made the commandment of God of none effect by your tradition."[122]

God praised the genuine love that Jacob had for Rachel, which he demonstrated in a seven-year wait that "seemed unto him but a few days, for the love he had to her."[128]

Love can always wait to give. However, lust can never wait to get.

Love is longsuffering and kind. It does not pursue selfish advantage. It never fails.[129]

Love is not just an emotion but a choice we make based on God's Will.

7. Honor Marriage

"What therefore God hath joined together, let not man put asunder."[123]

Resulting Quality: Loyalty

A correct view of marriage will be a giant step toward conquering lust, because marriage is the only way to fulfill sexual desires without guilt. Whenever you are tempted to lust, you can turn the temptation into a prayer of thanks to God for the normal desires that He has given for marriage and of dedication of single years for undistracted ministry.

By bringing sensual desires under the control of the Holy Spirit, these drives are transformed into spiritual energy.[124]

Acknowledge the transfer of power.

Most couples have no idea what Paul means when he writes, "The wife hath not power of her own body, but the husband: and likewise also the husband hath not power of his own body, but the wife."[125]

The Greek word for *power* in this verse is *exousiazō*, which means "to control, to exercise authority upon." This means that a husband cannot decide to look at pornography, because his wife has jurisdiction over his eyes. A wife cannot go out with her pastor or spend hours talking on the phone to a male friend, because her husband has jurisdiction over her feet and ears.

Avoid disillusionment in marriage.

If any man or woman thinks that he or she will satisfy abnormal sexual desires in marriage, he or she will be disillusioned. If this were true, a married person would never look lustfully at another person.

Based on this, a man must develop self-control before he gets married. During marriage, he must then use the disciplines of prayer and fasting to maintain self-control.[126] In this way, the marriage bed is kept honorable and undefiled, and both marriage partners are fulfilled, because their goal is not to get but to give.[127]

Personal Application

- ☐ Have I viewed marriage as a way to satisfy abnormal sensual desires?
- ☐ When I am tempted to lust, do I thank God for normal marriage desires and pray for God to bless the one He has chosen for me?
- ☐ Do I understand and agree that marriage gives the jurisdiction of my body to my spouse?
- ☐ If I am single, how long am I willing to wait to make myself ready to give to my marriage partner, meanwhile building personal disciplines?

Bitterness

How we deny or reveal bitterness

"I am not bitter . . ."

"I am just deeply hurt."
"I resent what they did."
"Offenders are repulsive to me."
"I can't forget what they did."
"I keep reliving their hurts."
"Any reminder reopens wounds."
"I hope they suffer like I do."
"What happened was not fair."
"I can't trust God anymore."

Ways we reveal bitterness

Harsh, vitriolic speech
Cutting off spirit to offender
Suicidal thoughts and actions
Being very easily offended
Quickly jumping to conclusions
Violent reaction to hurts
Being extremely judgmental
Taking up offenses for others
Hard facial features

How to Resolve

Bitterness

Required Command	Resulting Quality
Await My Return Matthew 24:42–44	**Punctuality** vs. Tardiness
Deny Yourself Luke 9:23–25	**Determination** vs. Faintheartedness
Love Your Neighbor Matthew 22:39–40	**Gentleness** vs. Harshness
Be a Servant of All Matthew 20:26–28	**Availability** vs. Self-Centeredness
Increase Your Faith Matthew 21:21–22	**Patience** vs. Restlessness
Forgive Your Offenders Matthew 18:21–22	**Forgiveness** vs. Bitterness
Despise Not Children Matthew 18:10	**Tolerance** vs. Condemnation

14

How Does Bitterness Affect the Digestive System?

The digestive process begins in the mind. As you think about specific foods, secretions begin to prepare your digestive tract for what you plan to eat. The digestive system provides the body with a continual supply of water, electrolytes, and nutrients. It plays a vital part in detoxifying and removing the body's waste products.

The entire digestive tract is technically outside the body. What goes through the tract only becomes part of the body when it is absorbed through its walls.

Of all the major systems of the body, the digestive system has the greatest interaction with the outside world. If the digestive tract were to be spread out, it would have a surface area roughly equal to that of a tennis court![1]

How the Defense System Can Turn Against the Body

One important function of the gastrointestinal tract is its defense against opportunistic organisms and toxic substances. The first line of this defense is the integrity of the intestinal lining.

Any compromise of the lining due to toxins and infectious agents decreases its ability to keep foreign substances out of the vital organs. When these foreign substances (antigens) cross this barrier,[2] they are recognized by a complex system called the gut-associated lymphoid tissue (GALT). Approximately 60% of the immune system and more than 80% of immature antibody-producing cells are located within the inner lining of the digestive tract.[3,4]

This process has been linked to food sensitivities,[5] inflammatory diseases,[6] and autoimmune diseases.[7,8] Thus if the digestive system is not functioning properly, it will cause great damage to a person's health and well-being.

Case Study of Bitterness

When Diane was seventeen years old, she began to have digestive problems. She did not stop to consider the causes; instead, she tried to deal with the problem by taking an antacid tablet to neutralize the acid. The antacid failed to bring relief, so she obtained a prescription for a drug that actually blocked acid production in her stomach.

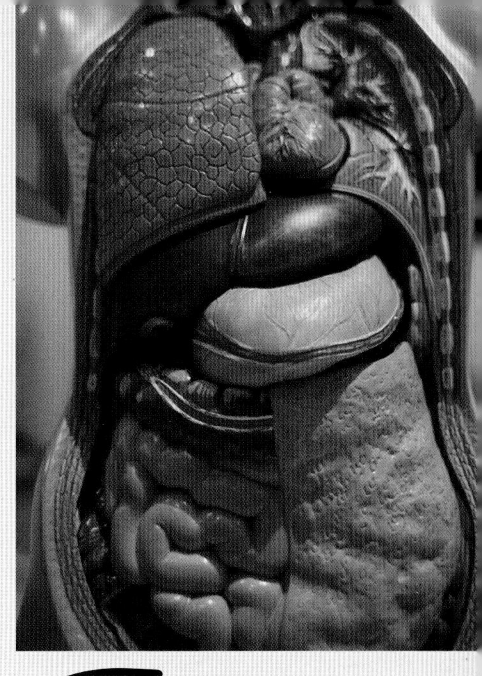

The digestive system is a complex network that provides the first line of defense against food antigens and pathogenic bacteria.[9] Any bitterness directly affects its ability to function.

The organs of the gastrointestinal tract include the mouth, pharynx, esophagus, stomach, intestines, and accessory organs (liver, gallbladder, and pancreas).

The gastrointestinal tract can be viewed as the third intelligence center of the body, along with the heart and the mind.

One hundred million neurotransmitters line the length of the gut, approximately the same number that is found in the brain.[10]

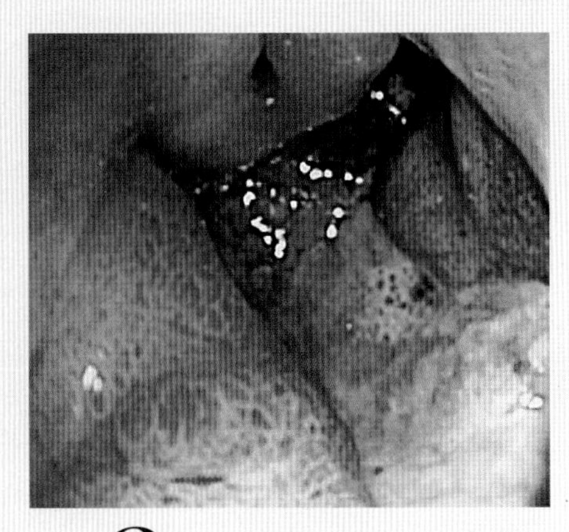

Stomach ulcers may be painful tormentors that result from the bitterness we allow by refusing to forgive.

The stress of bitterness decreases alkaline secretions that protect the stomach lining, at the same time increasing gastric secretions, which cause damage to the lining.

A Case Study

"My parents promised that when I reached the legal age, they would let me get my driver's license. When they broke their promise, I became bitter. Soon I developed stomach ulcers. I lost so much blood that I passed out and had to be hospitalized three different times.

"When I learned how my bitterness was causing my stomach ulcers, I asked my parents to forgive me. There is now no more anger, bitterness, or ulcers."

—Testimony from Teddy Lee

"Shouldest not thou also have had compassion on thy fellow servant, even as I had pity on thee? And his lord was wroth, and delivered him to the tormentors."[17]

Years went by and she learned to live with her problem. But then her situation became acute: a large tumor developed in her stomach. One day the tumor ruptured. She vomited blood and then fainted with excruciating pain.

Diane was rushed to the hospital for treatment. This was followed by the attempts of many doctors to figure out a cause and a remedy for her condition. When Diane learned that bitterness has a direct effect on the digestive system, she exclaimed, "That is my problem!"

When she was sixteen years of age, her moral standards were violated by a boyfriend. Ever since then, she had been bitter toward him. This bitterness directly affected her digestive system.

Bitter Memories

For nearly fifty years, we have begun the Thursday evening session of the Basic Youth Conflicts Seminar with a question: How many of you have been deeply hurt or offended by someone in your past?

More than 2 million youth and adults have given the same response. They immediately raised their hands to indicate that this had happened to them. We then pointed out the significance of their response. It was not in the fact that they had been offended, because most of us have experienced offenses of one sort or another. The real significance of their response was that they could recall the offense so quickly.

No doubt we have all heard the familiar phrase "just forgive and forget!" Unfortunately, most people do not understand how to forgive, and it is impossible to forget. Each time you remember past hurts, the wounds are reopened, the offense is relived, the tears well up, and the bitterness goes deeper into your soul.

This happens because there is an emotional memory in the limbic system of the brain. It stores all past memories so that they are never forgotten.[11] Events that you perceive as traumatic will have a continuing effect on your system, even though you may forget them.

How Bitterness Causes Ulcers

When you are stressed due to bitterness, even if it is subconscious, your autonomic nervous system becomes imbalanced.

This decreases alkaline secretions. Alkaline secretions are a buffer to protect the stomach from its own acids. With the natural protection decreased, the acid is able to erode into the stomach lining, producing esophageal, gastric, or duodenal ulcers.[12]

On the other hand, emotional stimuli such as bitterness produce a sustained increase in the gastric secretions of hydrochloric acid via the vagal nerve. This abnormal level of acid is then able to cause damage to the unprotected stomach lining.[13]

Bacteria can grow in the stomach in an environment with a pH between 1 and 3. Furthermore, bacteria have now been found to be one cause of ulcer formation, surviving even in the highest stomach acids.

Stress has not only been shown to suppress the response of the immune system to such pathogens, it has also been shown to increase the ability of bacteria to adhere to the digestive tract.[14]

This gives the opportunity for bacteria to penetrate the gastric mucosa, further changing the protective secretions and allowing acid to damage the lining of the intestine and stomach.[15,16]

How Stress Causes Liver Problems and Gallstones

The gallbladder is an organ that is tucked just under the front of the liver. It stores the bile secreted by the liver and provides the enzymes that break down the fats in the intestines.

The bile system in the body is affected by the stress of bitterness. When under stress, the walls of the gallbladder and the digestive tract relax. This can cause a "sluggish" digestive system, which slows the elimination of toxins in the bile, giving them a greater opportunity to be reabsorbed.[17] This increase in transit time has been associated with increased risk for hepatobiliary disease such as gallstones.[18]

Studies have shown that the release of stress hormones, as from bitterness, causes a decrease in the blood flow to the liver.[19] This has the obvious result of hindering the detoxification process of the liver, causing a buildup of harmful toxins in the body.

This sheds light on Solomon's observation in Proverbs 15:17: "Better is a dinner of herbs where love is, than a stalled ox and hatred therewith." There is no need to detoxify herbs, but the digestion of the fat of the ox would be hindered by the sluggish gallbladder that results from the stress of hatred.

The gallbladder has the capability to concentrate bile up to twenty times its original strength. This is more likely to happen if the bile is not fully expressed into the digestive tract. This process increases the possibility of gallstone formation.[20]

This coincides well with the meaning of Job 20:14: "His meat in his bowels is turned, it is the gall of asps within him." The Hebrew word translated *gall* also means "venom," another word for *toxin.*

Bitterness is one of the most common stresses among people today. It is therefore significant that one of the most common surgeries on the digestive tract is the removal of the gallbladder (cholecystectomy).

More than half a million people a year have their gallbladders removed.[21] This operation creates further problems, such as bile acid diarrhea, an increased risk of colon cancer, and the possibility of bile leakage, which produces agonizing stomach pains that necessitate emergency surgery.

How Bitterness Destroys Faith

Faith is a vital component to health and healing. This was emphasized by Jesus when He said to several whom He healed, "Thy faith hath made thee whole."[22]

In Mark 11, Jesus challenged His disciples to have faith, through which they could do great things.[23] However, He concluded His message with this instruction: "Therefore I say unto you, What things soever ye desire, when ye pray, believe that ye receive them, and ye shall have them. And when ye stand praying, forgive, if ye have aught against any: that your Father also which is in heaven may forgive you your trespasses. But if ye do not forgive, neither will your Father which is in heaven forgive your trespasses."[24]

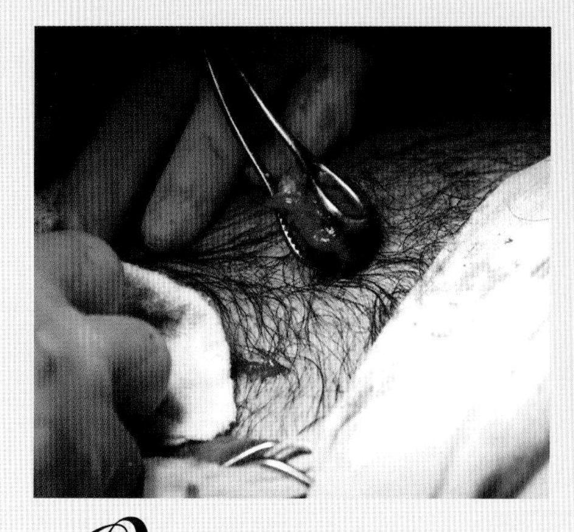

One of the most common operations today is the removal of the gallbladder, which can result in serious, unexpected complications.[25]

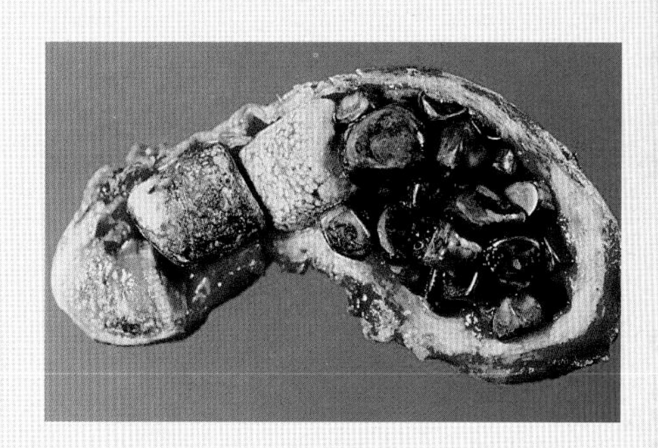

Stress slows down the gallbladder's effectiveness in eliminating toxins, which can lead to the formation of gallstones.

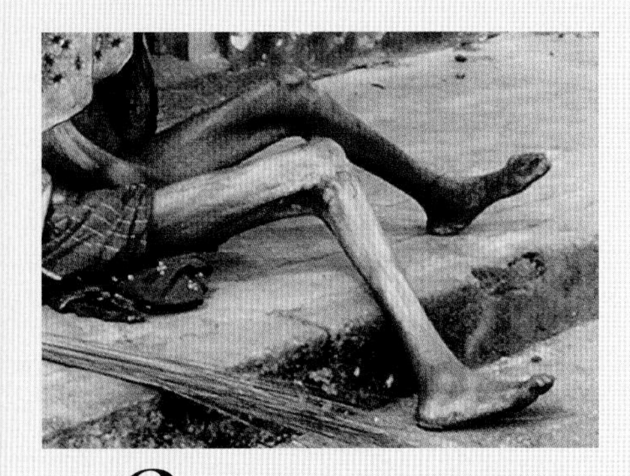

Starvation and obesity have the same root problem—a lack of enough nutritious food to keep the body healthy.

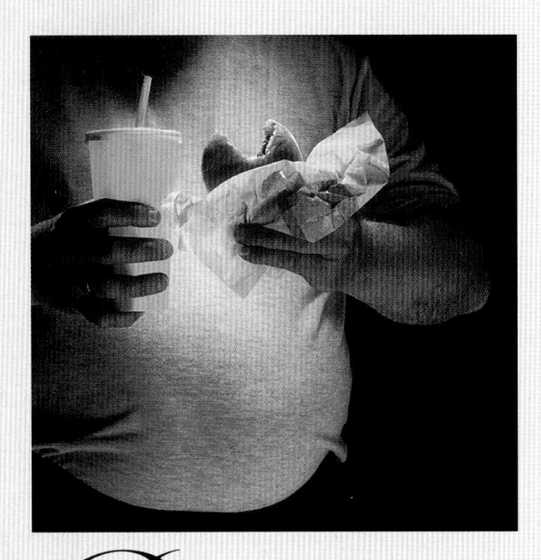

Bitterness produces stress, which upsets the hormonal balance and increases the level of cortisol. This decreases the hormone production in the thyroid and stimulates the appetite, resulting in obesity.[33,34]

Meanwhile, the body is starving for nutritious food and storing the toxic food in fat cells, further contributing to obesity.

How Bitterness Torments

Not only will bitterness block God's forgiveness of our transgressions; it will cause God to turn us over to mental, emotional, physical, and spiritual tormentors. Jesus warns about this in His graphic account of a wicked servant who was released from a huge debt but then refused to release a fellow servant from a small debt.

"And his lord was wroth, and delivered him to the tormentors, till he should pay all that was due unto him. So likewise shall my heavenly Father do also unto you, if ye from your hearts forgive not every one his brother their trespasses."[26]

How Bitterness Contributes to Obesity

One factor that contributes to obesity is hormone imbalance. Bitterness is perceived by the body as a stress, which elevates cortisol and inhibits thyroid hormone production.[27] This, in turn, stimulates the appetite and changes the metabolism of the body toward fat storage.[28,29]

The obvious result is an increase in weight, which for many people becomes a "tormentor" that brings other physiological, psychological, and spiritual problems.

How Bitterness Can Hinder Conception

Scripture makes a connection between infertility and bitterness in the account of David's wife Michal. After David blessed all the people, he returned to his house to give his family a blessing.

However, Michal had watched him through the window and despised him for his dancing. Because of her bitterness, God closed her womb. "Therefore Michal the daughter of Saul had no child unto the day of her death."[30]

There are medical factors that may have played a part in this case. Fertility is dependent on a delicate balance of hormones, which are released from the brain. These induce ovulation. Stresses such as bitterness have been associated with imbalance in these hormones, which results in infertility.[31,32]

Infertility among women is a major problem in America. Many who desperately want children are going to fertility experts and resorting to extreme measures to conceive. Many other couples are adopting. Once adoptive parents have a child, the stress of childlessness is removed, and many then conceive their own children.

A Significant Case of Cruel Tormentors

One of the most dramatic illustrations of how bitterness affects the digestive system took place in the life of Teresa Apple. Her story is very significant, and we can draw many insights and lessons from it. Therefore, we are giving the full text of her husband's account.

Teresa Apple

"Teresa had been suffering night and day for more than two and a half years. She had been unable to sleep more than one or two hours a night. It was an unrelenting ache that stole her joy and crippled her ability to function.

"Many people had prayed for her healing, but nothing happened. In the time of severest suffering, she would cry out for the pain to stop, but it continued.

"We also sought medical advice. The doctors ran a multitude of diagnostic tests, endoscopies, CT scans, and MRI scans. Hospital specialists ran batteries of blood tests, inserted overnight tubes into her esophagus, and conjectured over all manner of possible causes.

"Some said, 'classic acid reflux;' others, 'classic gallbladder problems;' still others, 'hiatal hernia issues.' Our primary care physician believed the best route was to remove Teresa's gallbladder. That would surely fix it, she was assured.

"She went to a surgeon who did what surgeons do best—remove organs or tissues. He comforted her by saying that she would feel great in a day or two. After the surgery, Teresa complained that the same pains existed. They never went away. When we went to the surgeon and told him, he said, 'It will just take time,' and sent us off to our primary care doctor.

"One of the gastroenterologists felt certain that Teresa had a hiatal hernia and prescribed acid blockers. When one failed, another one was given, until we had exhausted more than a dozen new drugs and spent thousands of dollars. None were remotely successful, and all had severe side effects that required additional drugs to counteract.

" 'How about a second opinion gastroenterologist?' Sure, no problem. So after months of excruciating pain and needless surgery, we were off to a new set of doctors.

"It was the same procedures as before, but this time we were told it was not a hiatal hernia, and no signs of acid reflux existed. During the office visit, the female doctor asked me to step out so she could talk alone to my wife. She was kindly and gently trying to get a confession that I was an abusive husband putting undue strain on our marriage. When that discussion closed unsuccessfully, I was ushered back in and we were told that this was all just psychosomatic—'just in your head.' They prescribed antidepressants and biofeedback training since the pain was only in her head. *Enough!*

"The pain was just as bad, if not worse. Medical solutions were exhausted. Doctors had been kind but were just guessing. Teresa was beginning to believe that she had an undiscovered cancer that would soon take her home. She began to cry that she hated not being there for me and watching our children grow up.

"Teresa began searching the Internet and joining e-mail loops for this kind of infirmity. Then began the steady number of herbal concoctions coming to our home. Our house began to look like a pharmacy. Bottles of high-powered prescriptions and powders lined the walls and took up all available counter space. Some had to be refrigerated, so we consumed most of our door shelving as well.

"At bedtime, my wife could only find relief by sitting nearly upright. She would be two feet above me in our bed with a heating pad behind her back. We never stopped praying. We had a new library, and my wife was fast becoming an expert on nutrients,

Freedom From the Pain of Sexual Abuse

Amanda was so emotionally devastated over past sexual abuse that she sobbed whenever it was mentioned. After explaining that God created her with a spirit, soul, and body, we asked her, "Which part is most important?" She said, "My spirit." "Which is the next most important?" She said, "My soul." "Which is the least important?" She said, "My body."

Then she was asked, "Why would God allow your body to be damaged?" She did not know, so we explained: "God compensates for losses. If He allows your body to be damaged, He gives you the potential to have a more powerful spirit, as He did for Daniel, whose captors made him a eunuch."

We asked, "If you had a choice of an undamaged body and a normal spirit, or a damaged body and a more powerful spirit, what would you choose?"

She said, "A more powerful spirit!" Then she dedicated her body to God. Thus it was not her body that the boys had damaged but God's body (retroactively), which is a far greater offense.

Next she verbally blessed her offenders by asking God to give them qualities they were obviously lacking, such as repentance, compassion, self-control, and love. Finally, she forgave them. Then she was asked, "How do you feel?" A huge smile broke over her face as she replied, "I feel like a bird soaring up to God! I am free! I am free!"

Courtesy of www.SolveFamilyProblems.com

Roots of bitterness usually begin with the deep hurts of family conflicts

King Jehoram is a prime example of this. He was obviously bitter with his brothers, because when he became king, he murdered all of them and then followed the idolatrous practices of heathen nations.

God's judgment included an incurable disease in his bowels, which the prophet predicted: "Thou shalt have great sickness by disease of thy bowels, until thy bowels fall out by reason of the sickness day by day."[35]

This prediction came true. "The LORD smote him in his bowels with an incurable disease. And it came to pass, that in process of time, after the end of two years, his bowels fell out by reason of his sickness."[36]

"Put on therefore, as the elect of God, holy and beloved, bowels of mercies, kindness, humbleness of mind, meekness, longsuffering."[37]

herbs, and medicines and their use. But *nothing* worked!"

How It All Began

"We had a family tragedy when my dad, Teresa's real father figure, was brutally attacked in a robbery attempt. A gang of drug addicts seeking money left my dad in a coma with severe brain damage.

"Although doctors said it was hopeless, my family and I stayed by his side. To everyone's surprise (except ours), he did not die and started making slow progress.

"During this time, the police arrested the men responsible for the crime and after two lengthy trials and one hung jury, convictions were reached. No remorse was ever expressed by the attackers.

"In 1998, Dad had made so much progress that we were going to bring him home. He would never be the same, but he knew us and could do some simple tasks.

"Then, on the day before he was to be released, the rehab facility decided to perform a minor procedure in the local hospital. A nurse gave him too much food in his nightly feeding, and he aspirated into his lungs. Now he had more severe brain damage than after the assault. He became vegetative.

"We were devastated! My dad died in January 2001, and soon my wife's pain began."

How We Found Healing

"We heard about the work of Dr. T. C. McDaniel and contacted him. He sent us a packet of minerals, made several other recommendations, and for the first time, Teresa was able to get minor relief.

"Then we heard about a Total Health Seminar and signed up for it. We prayed and fasted for the seminar, seeking God to make Teresa whole. I needed my wife back! We were ecstatic to learn that Bill Gothard himself would be there. We had high hopes for a miracle.

"On the first full day, we were blessed that there was an open seat at our table for breakfast. Bill walked in and sat at our table. Almost immediately and without hesitation, he looked across the table at Teresa and asked how she was doing.

"As we shared our story, Bill noticed the tears flowing from my wife's eyes as she described the attack on her father-in-law. Then he explained several Biblical steps of action that she must take if she wanted freedom from her pain.

"She took my hand and, with many tears, prayed through those steps. Almost immediately, Teresa's countenance changed. Within the hour, her pains were totally gone.

"By that evening, she did not need any of the fifteen medications that she had been taking at each meal. That night she slept on a regular pillow rather than in her propped-up position.

"The next day, she joyfully reported to the whole group how God had healed her and how, for the first time in two and a half years, she was without pain

"Her miraculous relief has continued, and we are thrilled that through this training we have not only experienced physical healing but also spiritual healing in other areas.

How to Defeat Bitterness With Full Forgiveness

Teresa Apple's pain was the result of the belief system of her heart. The challenge at that breakfast meeting was to help her construct an entirely opposite belief system from which she could make wise decisions. This can be summarized in the following three concepts.

1. Recognize benefits from the tragedy.

Teresa could see no benefit in what had happened to her father-in-law. However, Scripture tells us that "all things work together for good to them that love God"[38] and that we are to give thanks to God for His purposes in the things He allows to happen.[39] Therefore, she was asked to consider several possible benefits, each of which she affirmed.

"Did this draw you closer to God? Did this draw your family closer together? Did it cause you to cherish and appreciate the people in your life? Did it teach you valuable lessons on serving others? Did it cause you to see the need for people to repent and respond to Christ's love?" At that moment, she thanked God for allowing the tragedy and for the benefits that He intended by allowing it to happen.

2. Impart God's power to offenders.

Those who caused the death of her father-in-law obviously lacked the character qualities of love, kindness, compassion, self-control, repentance, etc. She was asked if she would like to help those gang members develop these qualities, and she said yes. It was then explained that she could do it by asking God to bless them with the qualities they lacked.

This step is based on the truth that "Death and life are in the power of the tongue"[40] and that when we bless those who damage us, we impart to them a spiritual enablement to develop missing qualities. At the same time, our positive blessings neutralize the negative damage of their hurts, and we are able to experience emotional freedom.

She then prayed a beautiful verbal blessing, asking God to build the suggested qualities in their lives.

3. Choose to forgive and live with the scars.

The tormentors that she was experiencing—her pain, inability to sleep, etc.—were then identified. She was told that she would never solve the pain in her stomach until she removed the pain of her heart.

To forgive is to release an offender emotionally and choose to live with the scars. Jesus demonstrated this when He fully released us from our offenses and chose to have the scars of crucifixion in His resurrected body.[41] When Teresa realized this, she prayed and fully forgave her offenders. At that point, Teresa experienced freedom.

Courtesy of www.SolveFamilyProblems.com

The foundation of forgiveness is a recognition of the benefits that God intended in allowing tragedies to happen in our lives.

One day, eleven men found themselves in the cruel prison of a foreign land. They had been accused of a crime they did not commit with evidence that had been planted in their possessions.

All hope of freedom was gone, and they resigned themselves to becoming slaves. However, one asked the right question:

"Why did God let this happen to us?"

Another brother answered the question. His answer was accurate. Immediately they were freed and reunited with their family, including their brother, whom they had sold into slavery.[42]

Discovering Benefits

1. **What character qualities will this tragedy force me to develop?**
2. **What faults or blind spots will this allow me to see?**
3. **What lessons will this teach me that I can share with others?**

"For the Lord himself shall descend from heaven with a shout, with the voice of the archangel, and with the trump of God."[47]

"And the dead in Christ shall rise first: Then we which are alive and remain shall be caught up together with them in the clouds, to meet the Lord in the air: and so shall we ever be with the Lord."[48]

Courtesy of www.SolveFamilyProblems.com

"We must all appear before the judgment seat of Christ; that every one may receive the things done in his body, according to that he hath done, whether it be good or bad."[49]

"And God shall wipe away all tears from their eyes."[50]

Seven Commands to Conquer Bitterness

1. Await My Return

"Watch therefore: for ye know not what hour your Lord doth come."[43]

Resulting Quality: **Punctuality**

When Jesus returns, we all will be ashamed of our wrong responses to offenders, and we will regret with tears the loss of glorious rewards for correctly responding to hurts.

Anticipate the joy of God's rewards.

One way to solve bitterness is to look at our offenses and responses in the light of eternity. For example, if someone willfully damages your property, you would tend to become bitter. However, consider this praise of the early believers: "Ye . . . took joyfully the spoiling of your goods, knowing in yourselves that ye have in heaven a better and an enduring substance. Cast not away therefore your confidence, which hath great recompence of reward."[44]

The things that make us bitter last for a brief moment on earth, but the rewards that come from rightly responding to hurts will last throughout endless ages of eternity. With this in mind, Jesus said: "Blessed are ye, when men shall revile you, and persecute you, and shall say all manner of evil against you falsely, for my sake. Rejoice, and be exceeding glad: for great is your reward in heaven."[45]

Avoid the sorrow of wrong responses.

The Second Coming of Christ is identified in Scripture as the purifying hope. "We know that, when he shall appear, we shall be like him; for we shall see him as he is. And every man that hath this hope in him purifieth himself, even as he is pure."[46] This hope should motivate us to see ourselves and our responses as they will be seen by all the world at the judgment seat of Christ.

Personal Application

- ☐ Do I realize that the things that make me bitter are temporary but that my responses to them are eternal?
- ☐ Do I realize that one day I will stand before Christ to give an account for all my responses—good and bad?
- ☐ Am I aware that whatever I do to the least of other believers, I am doing to Jesus?
- ☐ With this in mind, what will my responses be to my offenders?

2. Deny Yourself

"If any man will come after me, let him deny himself, and take up his cross daily, and follow me."[51]

Resulting Quality: Determination

The principle of denying ourselves is foundational to our lives and our achievements, because we conquer by our death, not by our life. Paul explained this by saying that he was "Always bearing about in the body the dying of the Lord Jesus, that the life also of Jesus might be made manifest in our body. For we which live are always delivered unto death for Jesus' sake, that the life also of Jesus might be made manifest in our mortal flesh. So then death worketh in us, but life in you."[52]

Know what it means to deny yourself.

Our natural inclination is to think that we will experience life by guarding and protecting the things we enjoy. So we react to those who interfere with our pleasure. However, Jesus knows that the pathway to life is through death to self: "Whosoever will save his life shall lose it: but whosoever will lose his life for my sake, the same shall save it."[53]

There is a difference between self-denial and denying yourself. Self-denial is the temporary setting aside of some pleasure. Denying yourself is the permanent setting aside of your own life so that you can experience the powerful work of Christ in and through you.

The Greek word for *deny* is *aparneomai,* which denotes a putting away on thc part of the speaker. It means "to remove from oneself, to refuse, to disown, to withdraw from fellowship."[54] This would mean to remove from yourself whatever hinders your relationship with Christ and to withdraw yourself from the fellowship of those who refuse to deny themselves.

Embrace the motivation to take up your cross.

When Jesus took up His cross, He understood that He would suffer and die on it, but He looked beyond the cross to see the multitudes who would find freedom through His death.

Personal Application

- ☐ What people group does God want to reach through my life?
- ☐ Have I denied myself in order to bring life to these people?
- ☐ Are my responses to the hurts of others free from bitterness?
- ☐ Have I removed myself from the fellowship of bitter people, knowing that they will discourage my denial of self?

To deny yourself is to die to the impulse of reacting to offenders and instead give them a blessing.

"There is a way which seemeth right unto a man, but the end thereof are the ways of death."[55]

Notice that Jesus did not tell us to take up His cross but ours.

Our "crosses" involve the sacrifices that we must make in order to reach the people groups we ask God to give us.

"Looking unto Jesus . . . who for the joy that was set before him endured the cross, despising the shame."[56]

To love someone is to understand him.

If you were to ask a teenage girl, "Do you think your dad loves you?" she would probably say yes. But then if you were to ask, "Do you think your dad understands you?" she would probably say no. Her reason would likely be "He does not listen to me."

One of the greatest gifts we can give a neighbor is a listening heart.

Courtesy of www.SolveFamilyProblems.com

Our neighbors are those in our lives who are in need of help that we can give.

3. Love Your Neighbor

"Thou shalt love thy neighbor as thyself."[57]

Resulting Quality: **Gentleness**

One of the basic needs of every person is to be understood. Therefore, one of the root causes of bitterness is misunderstanding or misjudgment. Thus a primary way to love your neighbor is to take extra efforts to listen to his heart. God was pleased with Solomon's request for "an understanding heart."[58] The Hebrew word for *understanding* is *shâma'*, which means "to give undivided listening attention."[59]

Fulfill all the Law.

When Jesus was asked to name the greatest commandment, He answered, "Thou shalt love the Lord thy God with all thy heart, and with all thy soul, and with all thy mind."[60] Then He added another command, which He stated as equally important: "And the second is like unto it, Thou shalt love thy neighbor as thyself. On these two commandments hang all the law and the prophets."[61]

Paul saw in this second commandment the fulfillment of the first, because whatever you do to your neighbor you do to the Lord. Therefore, he declares: "Ye have been called unto liberty; only use not liberty for an occasion to the flesh, but by love serve one another. For all the law is fulfilled in one word, even in this; thou shalt love thy neighbor as thyself."[62]

Begin with your "closest neighbor."

The closest neighbor to every husband is his wife, and the greatest way to love her is to understand her. Her mind may seem like a paradox until he realizes that she thinks and expresses herself from four different perspectives: her mind, her emotions, her will, and her spirit.

These may seem contradictory to him, but they are perfectly logical to her. Each one needs to be heard before a response is given, because "he that answereth a matter before he heareth it, it is folly and shame unto him."[63]

So if a wife makes a statement expressing her thoughts, a husband should ask, "How do you feel about that?" (her emotions); and then "What do you think should be done?" (her will); and then "What do you think God wants you to do in this matter?" (her spirit).

Personal Application

- ☐ How do I feel when others misunderstand or misjudge me?
- ☐ Do I realize that others feel the same when they are misunderstood?
- ☐ Have I asked God to give me a hearing heart so that I can hear what people are really saying and then meet their needs?
- ☐ Do I treat others the way I would want them to treat me?

How to Have a Courageous Conversation

Courageous conversations happen in an environment in which each person feels safe in sharing what he really thinks. This is achieved via nonthreatening questions that are easy to answer. After the question is answered, the other party repeats the answer as he understood it.

Very often the one repeating the question will not repeat it accurately. When this happens, it must be restated until it is accurate. There is a special dynamic of unity that takes place when each partner hears the other explain exactly what he has said and what he is thinking.

These questions are not only effective in resolving deep hurts between husbands and wives but also between brothers and sisters, children and parents, employers and employees, and others.

1. *What is your most pressing issue?*

When the most pressing issue is identified, other issues fall into place. Once answered, the response should be, "What I hear you saying is . . . ."

2. *In addition to this, is there a deeper issue?*

The goal is to get to the real issue, which is often unspoken because of fear of rejection. The underlying issue of a wife is often "Am I valued?"

3. *How is this affecting you?*

This allows a husband to see the pain of the issue through her eyes.

4. *What will the future be like if nothing changes?*

This is usually a wake-up call to the consequences of doing nothing.

5. *What do you see as my responsibility in this issue?*

In response, there can be no explaining, complaining, or blaming.

6. *What do you see as your responsibility in this issue?*

This question turns a victim mentality into shared responsibility.

7. *What does the preferable future look like to you?*

This begins to give hope and to build vision together.

8. *What is the most powerful thing we can ask God to do for us?*

This affirms the recognition that only God can fulfill expectations.

9. *Based on this, what is the one thing we cannot fail to do?*

This identifies the major goal to resolve the conflict.

10. *What practical steps must we take to make this happen?*

This assigns specific responsibility to work out steps of action.

Chris and Anne Hogan are helping thousands of couples transform bitter hurts into loving unity.

"The courageous conversation exercise has been the one tool that has done more for us in helping us get to real issues and pursue each other's hearts than anything else we've ever done. Through that tool, we find ourselves moving toward each other and separating out the issues in a clearer way than ever before."

—a father from Florida

"A courageous conversation is the most inspirational and practical tool. It has initiated an achievable vision for a successful relationship in our marriage."

—a couple from New Zealand

After conducting his first courageous conversation with several daughters who were embroiled in a heated argument, one father enthusiastically wrote, "The matter was settled in a manner never before done in my house."

For further helpful information on how to conduct courageous conversations, visit Chris Hogan's Web site at www.noblecall.org.

It is not wrong to desire greatness. It is wrong to strive for it in our own way.

The truest test of being a servant is how we respond when we are treated like one!

Few men are honored more than Abraham Lincoln. His greatness was in his humility and servant's spirit.

4. Be a Servant of All

"But he that is greatest among you shall be your servant."[64]

Resulting Quality: Availability

Much bitterness has come from battles over leadership. Even the disciples bitterly argued over who would be chief among them. When the other ten heard that James and John tried to secure positions on the right and left hands of Jesus in His kingdom, "they were moved with indignation against the two brethren."[65]

It was then that Jesus gave the command, "Whosoever will be great among you, let him be your minister; And whosoever will be chief among you, let him be your servant."[66]

God has established a paradox of servanthood.

The degree of our greatness is determined by the number of people who will allow us to serve them. We begin by serving those whom God has placed over us. As we learn the skills of servanthood, that number will increase.

When Joseph began serving Potiphar, he was a slave. However, because Joseph had a servant's spirit and served with his whole heart, God blessed everything he did. Soon Potiphar put Joseph in charge of his entire household. Then his servant's spirit was tested as he was falsely accused and put into prison. From there he was given the opportunity to serve all of Egypt and surrounding nations.[67]

If Jacob would have served his older brother, he could have avoided years of hard labor and the bitter conflicts he had with his brother and father-in-law. They both reacted to Jacob because they saw that he was serving his own interests.

When you become excited about making other people successful, you have found the road to greatness; and when you exercise five essential qualities, you will achieve greatness. These qualities are initiative, diligence, creativity, wisdom, and enthusiasm.

Personal Application

- ☐ How many people am I serving right now in my life?
- ☐ Am I serving the leaders whom God has placed over me by praying for them, getting to know them, and encouraging them?
- ☐ Do I realize that by encouraging those who are in positions of leadership to do good, I am serving all who are under them?
- ☐ Have I reacted to people when they do not treat me with the respect I think I deserve?

5. Increase Your Faith

"If ye have faith and doubt not . . . it shall be done."[68]

Resulting Quality: **Patience**

God evaluates the size of our faith by our ability to forgive our offenders. We discover this principle when Jesus told Peter that he had to forgive his offenders of "seventy times seven" offenses.[69] It was then that the apostles pleaded, "Increase our faith."[70] We also see this concept illustrated when Jesus relates great faith to forgiving offenders.[71]

Have faith that God will punish offenders.

Peter was obviously frustrated—if not bitter—at his offenders when he asked Jesus how many times he had to forgive them. No doubt he reasoned that if he forgave them up to seven times, and they still did not change, he could then exercise vengeance on them.

Jesus assured Peter and all others that He will bring about ultimate justice: "It is impossible but that offenses will come: but woe unto him, through whom they come!"[72]

Have faith that words can do great things.

After instructing His disciples to forgive offenders, Jesus said, "If ye had faith as a grain of mustard seed, ye might say unto this sycamine tree, Be thou plucked up by the root, and be thou planted in the sea; and it should obey you."[73]

Satan will deceive you into believing that through your bitterness you will get even with your offenders or change their behavior. This will not happen by your bitterness but by words of blessing.

You must ask God to bless your offenders with the character qualities they are lacking. If you do this and ask God to remove the "mountains" that are hindering them from coming to the Lord, and do not doubt in your heart but believe that what you say will come to pass, you will receive whatever you ask for.[74] Jesus concludes this promise by saying, "When ye stand praying, forgive."[75]

Personal Application

- ☐ How great is my faith (based on the number of times I am willing to forgive an offender)?
- ☐ Do I desire justice for my offenders in order to punish them for their wrongdoing or to restore their relationships with God?
- ☐ Have I spoken verbal blessings over those who have offended me?
- ☐ Do I have the patience to let God do His transforming work in me and my offenders?

Mountain-moving faith is based on our ability to forgive offenders.

If faith could cause a sycamore tree to obey our words, could not our words also influence an offender?

Being bitter is like drinking poison and hoping our offenders will die.

*F*orgiveness is releasing an offender emotionally and choosing to live with the scars.

*T*he key to forgiveness is turning a disastrous offense into a memorial of positive symbols.

*T*he alternative to forgiveness is bondage with the cords of bitterness.

6. Forgive Your Offenders

"If ye forgive not men their trespasses, neither will your Father forgive your trespasses."[76]

Resulting Quality: **Forgiveness**

There are two kinds of forgiveness; one is from the mind, and the other is from the heart. Forgiving from the mind does not impress God, nor does it work. Just saying "I forgive you" does not relieve you from the emotional bondage of all the hurts that your offenders have caused.

True forgiveness must be far deeper than a mental exercise; it must come from the heart. Thus Jesus said of the servant who did not have heartfelt compassion for his offenders: "His lord was wroth, and delivered him to the tormentors till he should pay all that was due unto him. So likewise shall my heavenly Father do also unto you, if ye from your hearts forgive not every one his brother their trespasses."[77]

Forgive from your heart.

When a little boy gave his mother a bill for the chores that he had carried out that week, his mother wrote out another bill. In it she listed the years of sacrifice and the many hours of day-and-night service. It came to quite an amount. Then she wrote on the bottom: "Paid in full. Love, your Mom."

In the same way, when you hold a grudge against an offender, you are like that little boy wanting payment for what is due to you. You have completely overlooked the huge debt that you owe God and that He fully paid for you with the blood of His own precious Son.

Only as we comprehend this contrast will you be free to forgive your offenders. That freedom will be enhanced as you ask God to bless your offenders with needed qualities and list the benefits that God intended by allowing the offenses to happen to you.

A further important step is to turn the scars from the offenses into meaningful reminders of how much Christ has suffered for you and how much He wants you to sacrifice your life for others.

Personal Application

- ☐ When I forgive an offender, do I still have bad feelings toward him?
- ☐ Have I calculated the number of times I have sinned against the Lord and how much I owe Him?
- ☐ Have I compared my debt to God with the debt others owe me?
- ☐ What significance have I attached to the scars that will continue because of the wounds of my offenders?

7. Despise Not Children

"Take heed that ye despise not one of these little ones."[78]

Resulting Quality: **Tolerance**

Much anger and bitterness can be traced to failure to love children. Children should never be viewed as burdens but always as blessings from the Lord: "Lo, children are a heritage of the LORD: and the fruit of the womb is his reward."[79]

Because children belong to God, He lovingly watches over every one of them. Jesus stated, "In heaven their angels do always behold the face of my Father which is in heaven,"[80] and "Whoso shall receive one such little child in my name receiveth me."[81] This is an awesome thought!

Despising children can cause marriage conflicts.

God designed a woman with the incredible ability to conceive new life. Having children is thus an important part of her identity and fulfillment. If the husband wants marriage without children, this may be perceived by his wife as saying, "I want to enjoy what you can give me, and I do not want to share you with children." This may cause her to feel like she is simply an object for his physical fulfillment rather than a daughter of the King of Kings who has a sacred mission in life.

Despising children can cause family conflicts.

A mother was baffled by the behavior of her child. From the day he was born, he would try to push away from her. When she was asked if she wanted this child, she said no. This mother knew that her husband did not want children, so when the child was conceived, she felt his rejection and she passed that on to her child. She did not realize that her child could discern acceptance or rejection in her womb.

That child became very rebellious and caused anger and frustration in the home. But when the parents asked him to forgive them for their wrong response to his birth, he did forgive them, and a new level of harmony was established between them.

Personal Application

- ☐ Do I love children the way God loves them?
- ☐ Do I encourage couples to have as many children as God wants to give them and support them in any way possible?
- ☐ Have I learned the skill of turning the hearts of fathers to their children and the hearts of children to their fathers?
- ☐ Do I cherish, respect, and honor mothers?

Both physical and spiritual children are the heritage of the Lord.

Children are a fulfillment of a husband and wife becoming one flesh.

Children are like arrows in the hand of a mighty man. Happy is the man who has his quiver full of them.[82]

Depression and Discouragement

When discouragement or depression comes, quote the following Scripture passages aloud.

"They that wait upon the LORD shall renew their strength; they shall mount up with wings as eagles; they shall run, and not be weary; and they shall walk, and not faint."[89]

"Let us not be weary in well doing: for in due season we shall reap, if we faint not."[90]

"Why art thou cast down, O my soul? and why art thou disquieted within me? hope thou in God: for I shall yet praise him, who is the health of my countenance, and my God."[91]

"If thou faint in the day of adversity, thy strength is small."[92]

"Consider him that endured such contradiction of sinners against himself, lest ye be wearied and faint in your minds."[93]

"Wherefore lift up the hands which hang down, and the feeble knees; And make straight paths for your feet, lest that which is lame be turned out of the way; but let it rather be healed."[94]

Distinguish depression from discouragement.

Discouragement is an emotional response to circumstances that we perceive to be bad. It is a state of the soul. Depression is a deep-seated despair of life and the future. It is a condition of the spirit.

Discouragement	*Depression*
• **A condition of the soul**	• **A condition of the spirit**
• **Giving up calling**	• **Wanting to give up life**
• **Losing mental perspective**	• **Losing spiritual perspective**
• **Listening to Satan's lies**	• **Believing Satan's lies**

Understand depression.

There is a physiological explanation for depression. As stress increases, the thyroid slows down. This alters methylation, causing an imbalance in the neurotransmitters and resulting in depression.[83] One of the major causes of depression is using up emotional energy.

Depression requires treatment on the physical, mental, emotional, and spiritual levels. When Elijah had suicidal depression, God first put him into a deep sleep. Then He woke him up and fed him wholesome food and water. Then He put him back into a deep sleep. Then God directed him to a quiet place by a brook, where he could rest and reflect on Who God is.[84]

When Jonah had suicidal depression because of his great emotional drain, God reasoned with him in an attempt to turn his anger into compassion for the people of Nineveh.[85] Depression can be a result of focusing on ourselves rather than God's kingdom.

Renew emotional energy.

If you are losing emotional energy because of one of the seven stresses, you must resolve the stress before you can experience relief. If, on the other hand, you have used up your emotional energy in the process of doing good works, you should read through the Psalms and mark the passages that describe the way you feel. As you memorize and meditate on these sections, the discouragement or depression will usually lift.

A further important factor in dealing with depression is forcing yourself to have a grateful spirit. There is power in praise. David demonstrates this throughout the Psalms during times of discouragement, as he does in Psalm 103: "Bless the LORD, O my soul . . . who healeth all thy diseases."[86] "In every thing give thanks"[87] for "A merry heart maketh a cheerful countenance: but by sorrow of the heart the spirit is broken."[88]

Greed

How we deny or reveal greed

"I am not greedy, but . . ."

"I want to be rich."
"Money is my security."
"Things make me happy."
"I never have enough."
"I must save for 'rainy days.' "
"I want a better retirement."
"It takes money to make money."
"I can't afford to tithe."
"I need a loan to get ahead."
"I want to win the lottery."

Ways we reveal greed

Damaging relationships for money
Lowering standards for gain
Any form of gambling
Frequently talking about money
Inability to enjoy possessions
Grief over bad investments
Impulsive buying
Lack of gratefulness
Going into debt for wants
Get-rich-quick schemes

How to Resolve

Greed

Required Command	Resulting Quality
Do Great Works Matthew 5:14–16	**Generosity** vs. Stinginess
Lay Up Treasures Matthew 6:19–21	**Thriftiness** vs. Extravagance
Seek God's Kingdom Matthew 6:33	**Initiative** vs. Idleness
Beware of Covetousness Luke 12:15	**Contentment** vs. Covetousness
Bring In the Poor Luke 14:12–14	**Hospitality** vs. Unfriendliness
Ask, Seek, and Knock Matthew 7:7–8	**Resourcefulness** vs. Wastefulness
Render to Caesar Matthew 22:19–21	**Gratefulness** vs. Murmuring

15

How Does Greed Affect the Immune System?

The human body has the ability to resist almost all types of organisms or toxins that damage its tissues and organs. This capability is called immunity.

The immune system is divided into two parts. Innate immunity refers to the body's defenses that are fully developed at birth. These include macrophages, destructive acids and enzymes, skin barriers, special chemicals, and natural killer lymphocytes.

Acquired immunity is made up of specialized cells that form antibodies or lymphocytes which attack and destroy foreign bacteria or toxins. Acquired immunity is broken down into B lymphocytes and T lymphocytes,[1] both of which develop from stem cells in the bone marrow and are differentiated in other organs before migrating through the bloodstream to lodge in the lymph nodes and spleen.

There they wait for chemical signals that activate the T lymphocytes to identify and attack foreign proteins, including bacteria and viruses. Similarly, B lymphocytes produce specific antibodies that work together with T lymphocytes to destroy harmful agents.

A condition that produces stress can initially enhance the immune system, but when stress is continuous, as in the case of greed, the immune system is suppressed.[2,3]

The ability of the immune system to mount an adequate inflammatory response in the body is essential to our very existence. Stress produces imbalances in the immune system that result in the loss of regulatory control, leading to a variety of dysfunctions.

This imbalance is seen in autoimmune and chronic inflammatory diseases such as rheumatoid arthritis, eczema, and inflammatory bowel disease.[4,5] Inflammation is also associated with the development of obesity,[6] diabetes mellitus,[7] atherosclerosis,[8] depression,[9] and cancer.[10,11]

The Root of All Evil

Since health is totally dependent on the immune system, we must guard against anything that will damage it. Scripture identifies the love of money as a chief source of destruction, because it is the root of all evil.

"They that will be rich fall into temptation and a snare, and into many foolish and hurtful lusts, which drown men in destruction and perdition. For the love of money is the root of all evil: which while some coveted after, they have erred from the

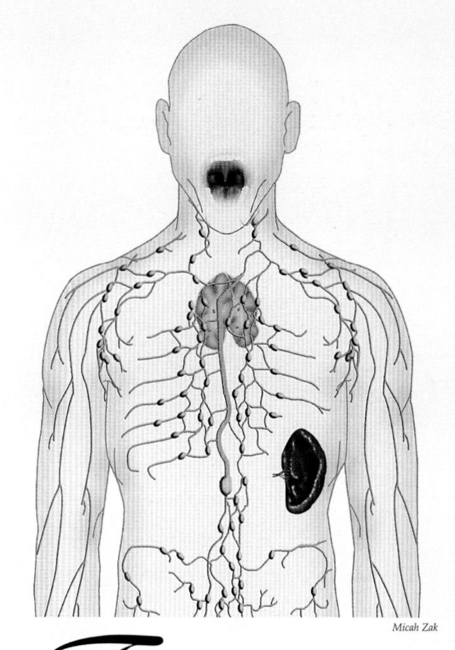
Micah Zak

The immune system is the body's defense against disease.

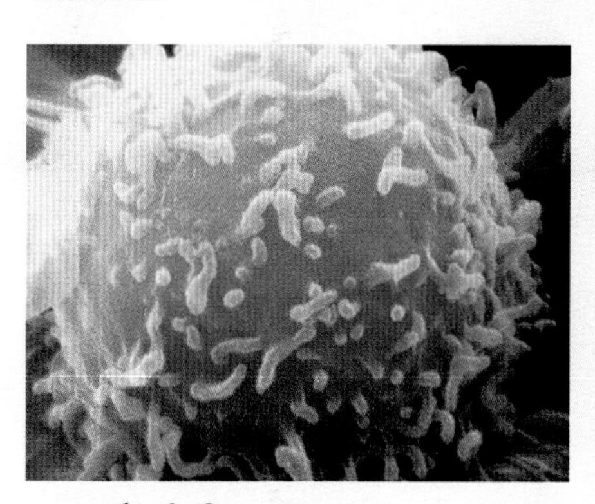

White blood cells, such as the lymphocyte pictured above, attack germs.

T lymphocytes are like armed soldiers, hunting out and destroying hostile agents in the blood.

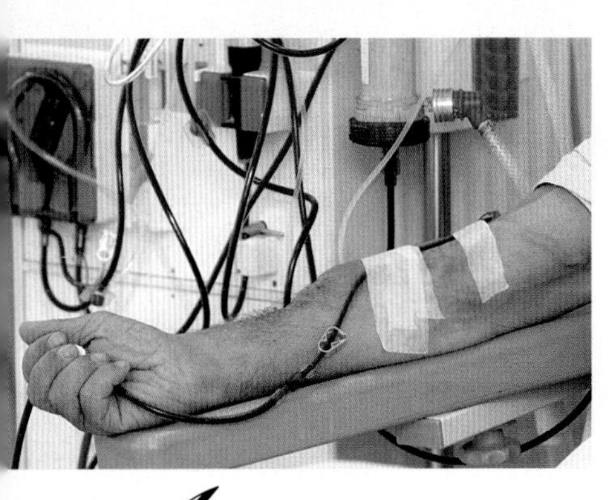

A new therapy cleanses the blood by exposing it to light.

"If thine eye be evil, thy whole body shall be full of darkness."[24]

Our wealth is not measured by how much we have but by how much we have invested in others.

Howard Hughes was one of the richest men in the world, yet he died as a reclusive drug addict, weighing only 93 pounds.[25]

faith, and pierced themselves through with many sorrows."[12] Notice the physical pain and anguish that accompany greed.

A greedy person is defined in Scripture as one who has an evil or stingy eye. Consider the warning that God gives to that person: "He that hasteth to be rich hath an evil eye, and considereth not that poverty shall come upon him."[13]

A greedy man will cause insecurity in his wife because she knows that he can lose all his money in one risky business venture. Also, when the children of a greedy man are asked, What do you think is more important to your dad: his job or you? they will almost always say, His job.

The sorrows that greedy people "pierce themselves through with" include health problems.

Anxiety Disorders

Greedy people do not get along well with others. Solomon points this out: "He that is greedy of gain troubleth his own house; but he that hateth gifts shall live."[14]

A greedy person is someone who expects money to do what only God can do. This includes providing security and happiness. Therefore, the god of a greedy person is money. Yet Scripture states that "riches certainly make themselves wings; they fly away as an eagle toward heaven."[15]

Sleep Disorders

Sixty million Americans suffer from sleep disorders. Americans now spend $3–5 billion annually on sleeping pills, which yield an average of only eleven extra minutes of sleep a night.[16,17]

The stress of financial pressure is a major contributing factor to sleep loss and all its accompanying sleep disorders. "The sleep of a laboring man is sweet, whether he eat little or much: but the abundance of the rich will not suffer him to sleep."[18]

Sleep is essential to maintain the balance of neurotransmitters in the body. A lack of sleep has been shown to have a detrimental effect on the immune system.[19,20]

Light Therapy

A new therapy has been developed that cleanses blood by means of light. As the blood passes through the light chambers, damaging agents are destroyed. This is similar to what takes place when mold is exposed to sunlight.

God links light in the body to a spirit of generosity and darkness to a spirit of greed: "The light of the body is the eye: if therefore thine eye be single, thy whole body shall be full of light. But if thine eye be evil, thy whole body shall be full of darkness."[21]

An Analogy of Greed

Rust is like a slow fire in metal, and radiation is a destructive burning in a patient's body.[22] With this in mind, notice the connection in the following passage.

"Your gold and silver is cankered; and the rust of them shall be a witness against you, and shall eat your flesh as it were fire. Ye have heaped treasure together for the last days.

"Behold, the hire of the laborers who have reaped down your fields, which is of you kept back by fraud, crieth: and the cries of them which have reaped are entered into the ears of the Lord of Sabaoth."[23]

How to Overcome Greed With a Spirit of Generosity

Greed begins with the false belief that money is the way to get honor, happiness, and security. The truth is that "By humility and the fear of the LORD are riches, and honor, and life."[26]

Greed is strengthened by the further false belief that we should obtain money through our own creativity and diligence. However, Scripture states, "It is he [God] that giveth thee power to get wealth."[27] A greedy person often fails to recognize the many reproofs that God brings into his life until he has a major financial loss or health problem.

Transfer ownership of all assets.

God protects what we dedicate to Him, because He then makes it most holy and sets it apart to be used only for His glory. What we keep for ourselves is vulnerable to "the devourer" and will be dissipated through the corruption of moths, rust, and thieves. By transferring the ownership of our time, energy, money, and possessions to God, we allow Him to not only protect them but also multiply them for His kingdom.

Learn contentment.

The secret to enjoying life and conquering greed is to be content with the basics of food and clothing. "Having food and raiment let us be therewith content."[28] Contentment allows us to enjoy what God has provided, whereas discontentment means that we are focusing on what He has not provided. Remember that window shopping and catalog browsing can become exercises in discontentment.

Become a sower.

God wants to demonstrate His love and supernatural power through the supply of money. In order for Him to do this, we must understand the concept of becoming "seed sowers."

A sower has two accounts: one for his personal needs, which he tries to keep to a minimum, and one to distribute to others. God has promised to multiply the seed money of a sower. "Now he that ministereth seed to the sower both minister bread for your food, and multiply your seed sown, and increase the fruits of your righteousness."[29]

This concept is distinctly different from a "prosperity gospel" message, which urges people to give so that God will provide new cars, expensive homes, and other luxury items for their personal indulgence.

In II Corinthians 9:9, Paul quotes Psalm 112 to explain sowing: "Blessed is the man that feareth the LORD, that delighteth greatly in his commandments. . . . Wealth and riches shall be in his house . . . He hath dispersed, he hath given to the poor; his righteousness endureth forever."[30]

Four uses of money:

1. **Meeting Basic Needs**
2. **Demonstrating God's Power**
3. **Uniting Believers**
4. **Giving Direction by Provision**

Courtesy of www.SolveFamilyProblems.com

The success of a sower is determined not by how much seed is in his bag but by how much is in the ground.

A sign on a country store read: "We have everything you need. If we don't have it, we'll explain to you why you don't need it."

Great works require us to invest personal assets in order to carry them out.

Good works become great works when they are done in the name of Jesus and draw people to His love and truth.

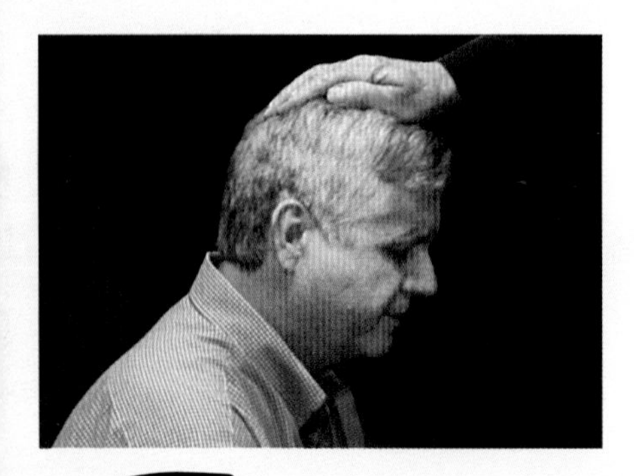

There is a treasure of power for great works when elders lay hands on us and commission us for ministry.

"Stir up the gift of God, which is in thee by the putting on of my hands."[42]

1. Do Great Works

"Let your light so shine before men, that they may see your good works."[31]

Resulting Quality: **Generosity**

God did not design us for greed but for great works: "For we are . . . created in Christ Jesus unto good works, which God hath before ordained that we should walk in them."[32] Jesus gave Himself for us, "that he might redeem us from all iniquity, and purify unto himself a peculiar [treasured] people, zealous of good works."[33] Therefore, we are to "provoke unto love and to good works"[34] and "be ready to every good work."[35]

Give light to the world.

Jesus did not say to His newly chosen disciples, "You will someday be the light of the world." He informed them, "Ye are the light of the world."[36] His instruction was to not hide their light under a bushel but to let it shine to the world through good works. With good works, we are able to silence those who falsely accuse our righteous way of life. Men will "see your good works, and glorify your Father which is in heaven."[37]

Turn good works into great works.

The good works that we are to carry out are the same as those that Jesus did when He lived on earth. He describes them: "The Spirit of the Lord is upon me, because he hath anointed me to preach the gospel to the poor; he hath sent me to heal the brokenhearted, to preach deliverance to the captives, and recovering of sight to the blind, to set at liberty them that are bruised, to preach the acceptable year of the Lord."[38]

Jesus said to His disciples, "He that believeth on me, the works that I do shall he do also; and greater works than these shall he do; because I go unto my Father."[39] Such works, however, can be accomplished only by the power of the Holy Spirit.[40] It is for this reason that the Apostle Paul laid his hands on Timothy and later said, "Stir up the gift of God, which is in thee by the putting on of my hands."[41]

Personal Application

- ☐ Do I comprehend the significance and responsibility of being the light of the world and accurately reflecting Christ?
- ☐ How would I rate my level of zeal to do great works for the Lord?
- ☐ Do I know what great works God wants to carry out through me during my lifetime?
- ☐ What resources am I willing to invest to carry out great works?

2. Lay Up Treasures

"Lay up for yourselves treasures in heaven, where neither moth nor rust doth corrupt, and where thieves do not break through nor steal."[43]

Resulting Quality: **Thriftiness**

Under the Old Covenant, God required His people to tithe the first part of all their income: "Bring ye all the tithes into the storehouse, that there may be meat in mine house."[44] God promised to bless all who did this: "Honor the Lord with thy substance, and with the firstfruits of all thine increase: So shall thy barns be filled with plenty."[45]

Under the New Covenant, God has a bigger and better "financial plan." He wants every believer to be a channel of His funds in order to fulfill our calling to bless all the families of the earth.[46]

Embrace God's financial plan.

God's New Covenant financial plan is explained in II Corinthians 8 and 9. It is based on the laws of the harvest: "He which soweth sparingly shall reap also sparingly; and he which soweth bountifully shall reap also bountifully."[47]

A seed sower sets aside what he needs for basic necessities and then establishes a special fund for good works: "God is able to make all grace abound toward you; that ye, always having all sufficiency in all things, may abound to every good work."[48] Under this arrangement, God promises to "multiply your seed sown, and increase the fruits of your righteousness."[49]

As we become sowers, God will enrich us "in every thing to all bountifulness, which causeth through us thanksgiving to God"[50] for our generosity. Then God will cause others to give to us, because generosity is contagious: "Give, and it shall be given unto you; good measure, pressed down, and shaken together, and running over, shall men give into your bosom."[51]

Personal Application

- ☐ Have I reduced my spending to just basic needs so that I can have more money to give to the needs of other people?
- ☐ Have I purposed that when God multiplies my income it is not for my wants but to give away at God's direction?
- ☐ Do I use discretion in distributing the funds that God provides for sowing so that I do not give it to those who will misuse it?
- ☐ Am I keeping records of God's provisions so that I can glorify God by telling others about the results?

One of the chief purposes of giving is to learn the fear of the Lord.[44]

Cristina began her "seed sowing" career by giving away what little she had. Then she began to receive unexpected funds amounting to thousands of dollars. When she received a grant from the Chicago Board of Education and explained her sowing to them, they asked her to tell her story to the public schools.

Pastor Ken Pierpont and his wife, Lois, dedicated themselves to become sowers. In the first eighteen months, God entrusted to them more than $40,000 of unexpected gifts to use for sowing.

3. Seek God's Kingdom

"Seek ye first the kingdom of God, and his righteousness; and all these things shall be added unto you."[53]

Resulting Quality: **Initiative**

The jurisdiction of God's future kingdom will include all the nations of the world. The jurisdiction of His present kingdom is to include our hearts.

It is unlikely that a greedy person has any comprehension of the kingdom of God. Nor is a person who worships money qualified to become a part of it, because no "covetous man, who is an idolater, hath any inheritance in the kingdom of Christ and of God."[54]

The kingdom of God is Christ's rule within us. A greedy person is ruled by the love of money. Jesus said: "No man can serve two masters: for either he will hate the one, and love the other; or else he will hold to the one, and despise the other. Ye cannot serve God and mammon."[55]

A greedy person puts money as his first priority, whereas the dedicated believer makes his first priority the kingdom of God. The riches of the greedy are consumed by "the devourer," but the wealth that comes from kingdom living lasts throughout eternity.

Find the secret of kingdom resources.

The law of the kingdom of God involves all the commands of Christ, and the resulting character qualities would be His righteousness. *Charakter* is the Greek word for the "express image" of Christ.[56]

When you live out the commands of Christ in your life and teach them to others, both you and the ones you teach will become true disciples of Christ: "If ye abide in me, and my words abide in you, ye shall ask what ye will, and it shall be done unto you. Herein is my Father glorified, that ye bear much fruit; so shall ye be my disciples."[57]

God will use the ones you disciple to open doors of future opportunity and provide needed finances. This is the principle that Paul both experienced and taught.[58] If you fail to make disciples first, you are simply cutting off "all these things" that God wants to add to your life through those you disciple.[59] Instead, you will be left to your own resources to try to pull together the finances that you need to live on.

Since God feeds the birds of the air and clothes the flowers of the field, will He not much more take care of you, "O, ye of little faith?"[60]

Personal Application

- ☐ Is my first priority in life to seek God's kingdom by learning, living out, and teaching His commands?
- ☐ Have I rejected the deceptive goal of building up personal assets for my future security?
- ☐ Is Christ ruling in my mind and my heart, and is His Word controlling every decision that I make regarding my assets?
- ☐ How many people am I discipling right now?

4. Beware of Covetousness

"Take heed and beware of covetousness."[61]

Resulting Quality: Contentment

Coveting is desiring something that God has decided not to give you. The tenth commandment speaks specifically about this destructive sin: "Thou shalt not covet thy neighbor's house, thou shalt not covet thy neighbor's wife, nor his manservant, nor his maidservant, nor his ox, nor his ass, nor any thing that is thy neighbor's."[62]

If you attach your affection to anything that belongs to your neighbor, you not only destroy your spirit of serving but also create a spirit of greed. Rather than being excited about making your neighbor successful, you are excited about making yourself prosperous. Therefore, Jesus explains the command not to covet by stating that "a man's life consisteth not in the abundance of the things which he possesseth."[63]

Then Jesus gives a parable of a rich man who, when his fields yielded an abundant crop, said to himself: "This will I do: I will pull down my barns and build greater; and there will I bestow all my fruits and my goods. And I will say to my soul, Soul, thou hast much goods laid up for many years; take thine ease, eat, drink, and be merry.

"But God said unto him, Thou fool, this night thy soul shall be required of thee: then whose shall those things be, which thou hast provided? So is he that layeth up treasure for himself, and is not rich toward God."[64]

Some things are worth "coveting."

You have the capability of delighting in anything you desire. If you delight in the "forbidden fruit" of things that are not beneficial to you, you will be destroyed. But if you delight in that which will make you more productive for God, you will be rewarded.

Thus Scripture says, "Delight thyself also in the LORD; and he shall give thee the desires of thine heart."[65] We are also to "covet earnestly the best gifts"[66] for ministry, and especially "covet to prophesy [proclaim God's truth]."[67]

Personal Application

- ☐ Do I desire anything that my neighbor owns?
- ☐ Am I trying to store up riches so that I can enjoy a comfortable retirement of pleasure?
- ☐ Do I have possessions that are rusting with disuse, getting moldy in storage, or so extravagant that I fear they would be stolen?
- ☐ How rich am I toward God?

God has only one retirement plan. It is called heaven.

When we cease to be effective on earth, there is no reason for us to remain here.

Our abundance is not for our personal indulgences but to sow into the lives of others and gain riches in heaven.

Before heaping up treasures for ourselves, we should ask, "Whose will these be when I die?"

To covet is to focus on our ambitions rather than the success of our neighbors.

"And seekest thou great things for thyself? seek them not."[68]

Imagine the honor of preparing a dinner with Jesus as your Guest! This is what we do when we bring in the poor.

"Inasmuch as ye have done it unto one of the least of these my brethren, ye have done it unto me."[73]

The staff at IBLP's Indianapolis Training Center faced a challenge of how to effectively connect with their neighbors. They asked the neighborhood association president if she would like to invite the neighbors in for a meal to honor them.

More than one hundred guests attended. They were so grateful for the dinner that they asked the staff to explain their mission and listened attentively to the message of Christ's salvation.

5. Bring In the Poor

"When thou makest a feast, call the poor, the maimed, the lame, the blind."[69]

Resulting Quality: Hospitality

Greed is the result of focusing on your own life. Thus one of the most effective ways to conquer greed is to see life through the hurts and pains of those who are living with great personal difficulties. One way to do this is to invite such people into your home for a special dinner and look for ways to honor them.

"Make a feast" with a purpose.

The first step in reaching out to the poor is to find common ground—everyone needs food. The second step is to find a way to make people feel special, not just recipients of charity. The next step is to provide a way to really get acquainted with the feelings, desires, questions, and problems of those who are in need. Discussion around a dinner table is an ideal place for this to happen.

It would be important to make your guests feel comfortable by designing appropriate questions and then listening with a "hearing heart." By investing in the poor, you will not only become their friend but will develop a love for them and a desire to further benefit them. "For where your treasure is, there will your heart be also."[70]

Recognize the rewards of a special dinner.

The first reward is a big step toward conquering greed. The next is the joy of giving, because "It is more blessed to give than to receive."[71] Then there is the reward of enlarging your stingy, hard heart and expanding your narrow, little world.

But the greatest reward is pleasing Jesus and having fruit that you can enjoy throughout all eternity: "Thou shalt be blessed; for they cannot recompense thee: for thou shalt be recompensed at the resurrection of the just."[72] Imagine having fellowship with your dinner guests in heaven when they have their resurrected bodies!

Personal Application

- ☐ **How many dinners have I held for the poor?**
- ☐ **Have I taken practical steps to find out who are poor in my neighborhood or city?**
- ☐ **Do I know how to design a meal that will make my guests feel safe in sharing their problems?**
- ☐ **Do I realize that sponsoring such dinners is the same as inviting Jesus into my home?**

6. Ask, Seek, and Knock

"Ask, and it shall be given you; seek, and ye shall find; knock, and it shall be opened unto you."[74]

Resulting Quality: **Resourcefulness**

The world of faith and the world of greed are two opposite realms. Faith desires to obtain things for God's kingdom, but greed desires to obtain things for one's own purposes. Greed must rely on our own abilities and efforts. Faith relies on God's ability to provide according to His Word.

God has assured us of provision.

The underlying motivation of both greed and faith is the need for food, clothing, and other essentials for living. God is certainly aware of our need for these things, but He wants us to ask for them every day. Thus He taught us to pray, "Give us this day our daily bread."[75]

God designed us with daily needs so we would keep our focus on Him as the great and loving Provider of all our needs. Paul states, "My God shall supply all your need according to his riches in glory by Christ Jesus."[76]

A greedy person does not have an intimate relationship with God, nor does he want to depend on God for daily provisions. He wants to be self-sufficient and independent. Thus his goal is to heap up treasures for future security.

Fulfill the prerequisites to obtain God's provision.

The first prerequisite to receive what you need from God is to ask Him for it aloud from your heart—"Ye have not, because ye ask not."[77]

The second prerequisite is to ask for things that will benefit God's kingdom, not your own selfish desires. "Ye ask, and receive not, because ye ask amiss, that ye may consume it upon your lusts."[78]

Some requests may take time before you see God's answer. The nation of Israel cried out for deliverance from bondage in Egypt, and God answered by sending them a baby named Moses. Moses delivered them eighty years later.[79]

Personal Application

- ☐ When I pray for something, do I pray using the name of God that corresponds to the request?
- ☐ Do I base my request on precise Scripture passages?
- ☐ Do I evaluate how my request will advance the work of God in bringing others to His love and truth?
- ☐ Am I willing to wait for God's timing in giving me an answer?

Faith is not a blind leap in the dark but a step based on the confidence that God will act according to the laws of His Word.

Faith overcomes the world in the same way that the law of aerodynamics "overcomes" the law of gravity.

We give offerings at church to support God's spiritual ministers, and we pay taxes to support God's civil ministers. "He is a minister of God to thee for good."[83]

A pastor in inner New York City asked the local police chief if he could pray for his officers before they went out on their shifts.

The chief quickly saw good results, so he asked the pastor to pray for the officers on all three shifts. Crime in that district began to plummet, and on Halloween night, traditionally the worst night of the year, there were no arrests![84]

7. Render to Caesar

"Render therefore unto Caesar the things which are Caesar's; and unto God the things that are God's."[80]

Resulting Quality: Gratefulness

One form of greed is refusal to pay taxes. Even some Christians have defended their right to do this by claiming that the Constitution supports their actions. However, they overlook the fact that believers are to obey not only the Constitution but also God's higher law.

God's "kingdom law" requires that all believers recognize that government officials are His ministers to carry out punishment on those who break His laws and praise on those who keep them.

"For he is the minister of God to thee for good. But if thou do that which is evil, be afraid; for he beareth not the sword in vain: for he is the minister of God, a revenger to execute wrath upon him that doeth evil.

"Wherefore ye must needs be subject, not only for wrath, but also for conscience sake. For for this cause pay ye tribute also: for they are God's ministers, attending continually upon this very thing. Render therefore to all their dues: tribute to whom tribute is due; custom to whom custom; fear to whom fear; honor to whom honor."[81]

We are to render to Caesar more than just money.

Not only are we to pay taxes and tribute to civil governments, but we are also to pray for all in authority. We are to pray for them so that "we may lead a quiet and peaceable life in all godliness and honesty. For this is good and acceptable in the sight of God our Savior; Who will have all men to be saved, and to come unto the knowledge of the truth."[82]

Ordinarily, we should not pay more taxes than are required of us. However, Jesus set the precedent of paying taxes that were technically not required of Him but the refusal of which would have offended the officials.

Taxes should be viewed not as a penalty for living in a country but as a payment to the ministers of God so that we can live in freedom to carry out His will.

Personal Application

- ☐ Do I recognize government officials as ministers of God and my taxes as supporting them to do good works?
- ☐ Do I promptly pay all my taxes and fees in order not to bring reproach on the name of Christ?
- ☐ Am I praying for the government officials that labor to protect and benefit my life so that I am able to serve the Lord?
- ☐ Have I expressed my appreciation for the diligent and faithful labor of government officials with a letter or an appropriate gift?

Fear

How we deny or reveal fear

"I am not fearful . . ."	**Ways we reveal fear**
"I am just concerned."	Eyes widening
"I tend to worry."	Trembling and shaking
"People frighten me."	Fingernail biting
"Everyone has fears."	Flushed face
"I just want it all to be okay."	Insomnia
"I can't control the situation."	Cold sweating
"I was only startled."	Racing pulse
"I tend to imagine the worst."	Panic attacks or asthma
"I'm worried about others' opinions."	Excessive insurance
	Peer dependence

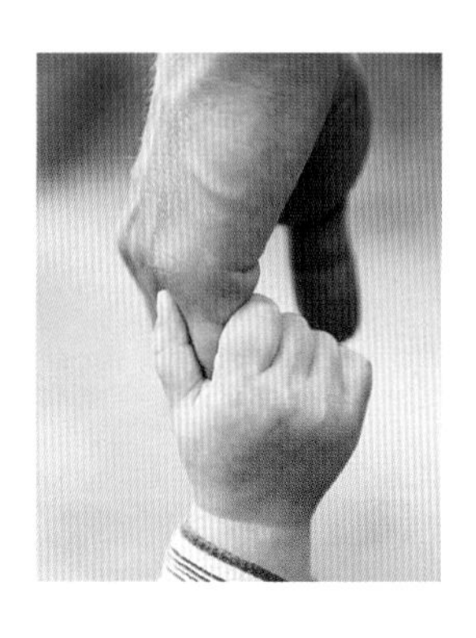

How to Resolve

Required Command	Resulting Quality
Follow Me Matthew 4:19	**Meekness** vs. Anger
Take My Yoke Matthew 11:28–30	**Obedience** vs. Willfulness
Be Wise as Serpents Matthew 10:16	**Wisdom** vs. Foolishness
Be a House of Prayer Matthew 21:13	**Persuasiveness** vs. Contentiousness
Receive God's Power Luke 24:49	**Orderliness** vs. Confusion
Watch and Pray Matthew 26:41	**Endurance** vs. Discouragement
Fear Not Matthew 10:28	**Boldness** vs. Fearfulness

16

How Does Fear Affect the Respiratory System?

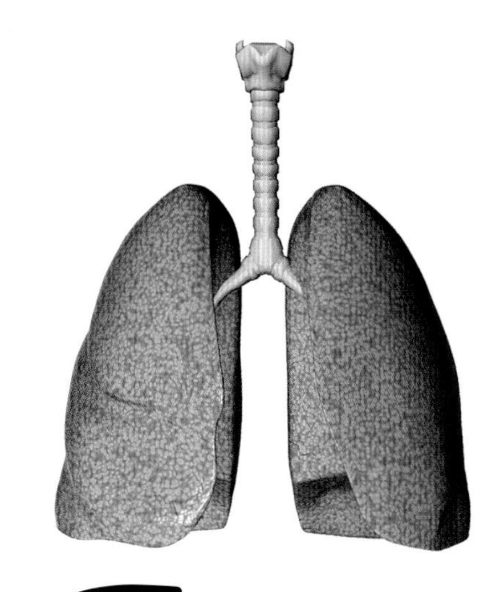

The major functions of the respiratory system are to provide oxygen to every cell in the body and to remove carbon dioxide from the blood. This amazing process takes place as we inhale clean air through the nose and mouth and exhale carbon dioxide from the lungs.

As we inhale, life-giving oxygen it is brought into small chambers (alveoli) that are surrounded by many blood vessels. The oxygen diffuses across the lung lining directly into the bloodstream, where it is carried by red blood cells throughout the body.

In certain respiratory conditions, such as asthma, the transfer of oxygen is hindered by mucus production and increased airway resistance.

The Pervasiveness of Fear

When God states something once in the Bible, it is important. When He says it twice, it is very important. But when He repeats a command more than one hundred times, we had better stop and listen to what He is saying. This is the case with His command to "fear not" or "be not afraid."

We all tend to live in a state of fear. An obvious example of this occurs when an employee is unexpectedly called into the president's office. What do you think his first response would be? No doubt, a sudden fear would strike through his heart and he would say to himself, "What did I do wrong?"

Why would this be his natural response rather than saying to himself: "Well, it is about time! My boss has finally seen how valuable I am to this company, and he no doubt wants to give me a raise!"? There are many situations in life that cause people to immediately think the worst.

However, anyone who fears the Lord and delights greatly in His commands "shall not be afraid of evil tidings: his heart is fixed, trusting in the LORD: his heart is established, he shall not be afraid."[1]

Jesus continually had to remind His disciples, "Fear not," because fear was their natural response to every unknown situation. There are many types of fears—fear of rejection, fear of failure, fear of the future, fear of abandonment, fear of evil, fear of sickness, fear of death, etc.

Each fear has its roots in the lies of Satan and can be overcome when we understand God's truth. "Ye shall know the truth, and the truth shall make you free."[2]

The respiratory system facilitates the movement of air in and out of the body through the nasal passage, pharynx, larynx, trachea, thoracic cavity, bronchi, and 300 million alveoli.

The more we fear the Lord, the less we will fear people. The less we fear the Lord, the more we will fear people.

Fear is like an old lion that roars to scare its prey to the younger lions lurking in the tall grass.

Mongolia became one of the largest empires in history because their fearless warriors struck terror in the hearts of their enemies.

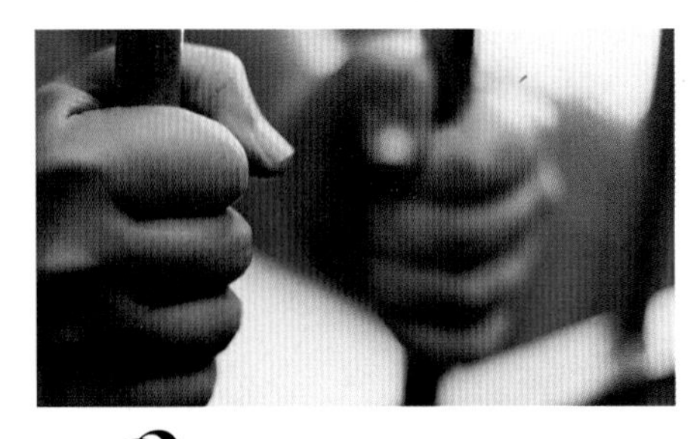

Only God's truth can set us free from the prison of fear.

Fear Is Contagious

Not only is fear damaging to our lives, but we can pass it on to those around us, damaging their lives as well. For this reason, God commanded the generals of Israel to declare to the army before a battle, "What man is there that is fearful and fainthearted? let him go and return unto his house, lest his brethren's heart faint as well as his heart."[3]

Fear Affects Health

A medical doctor in Texas met with a patient who had recurrent asthma symptoms and prescribed a treatment. However, after a while she returned with no improvement in her condition. A second remedy was prescribed, but once again she came back to the doctor.

After the third visit, the doctor said, "My solutions are not working. Do you have any stress in your life?" She began to reveal the personal problems that she was going through at that time. At the root of these problems was fear.

The doctor had a preliminary copy of this book and opened it to this section on fear. When she saw the connection between her respiratory problems and fear, she was amazed and asked the doctor for a copy of the book so that she could resolve her stress of fear.

The lungs and skin each have a unique response to the stress of fear through the immune and autonomic nervous systems.[4,5]

Researchers have found that stress perception is translated to skin not only by classical stress hormones but also by certain neurotrophins and neuropeptides that produce inflammation. This likely contributes to the triggering and aggravation of immune-related skin diseases.[6,7,8,9]

Another connection between fear and skin can be seen when someone experiences an embarrassing situation. Immediately his skin will flush deep red, which often is an outward manifestation of inward fear.[10]

Fear Triggers Asthma

A pastor was playing a game with his little boy when he needed to return to the church for a few minutes. The son did not want him to leave and begged him to stay. However, the father assured his son that he would be back shortly and then left.

As the pastor was about to return home, the church phone rang, and he became involved in a long counseling situation. After about a half-hour, there was a knock at the door. There was his little boy, standing with tears running down his cheeks, asking his dad to return home.

Before long, that little boy developed asthma. Years later, the father learned how his son's asthma could well have been caused by a fear of abandonment.

An association between asthma and the fear of abandonment has been clearly established in many studies. In single-parent homes, asthma among the children is twice as prevalent as it is in homes with both parents.[11,12]

The underlying cause of asthma is a hypersensitive state of the airways associated with an imbalance in the immune system and nervous system.[13] This explains how stress and other triggers can result in the narrowing of the airways and a buildup of mucus and carbon dioxide.[14] In this condition, air can be freely inhaled, but is blocked from being exhaled.

How to Cast Out Fear With Perfect Love

1. Fear of Rejection

Most teenagers fear the rejection of their peers more than the disapproval of God or their parents. As a result, many will surrender their moral purity, contract devastating diseases, become involved in drugs, or disfigure their bodies with lifelong tattoos.

This fear could be conquered if they were to discover the life purpose God has for them, dedicate their body to God, bond with wise and Godly friends, and learn to stand alone for what is right. The ability to stand alone is the heritage of those who know that they are following God's superior way of life.

2. Fear of the Unknown

Many surveys have been taken to determine the most stressful events in life. Moving to a new location ranks consistently high, especially among women. One woman had a major problem with food allergies. Out of one hundred foods, she could eat only ten. She realized that her allergies flared up just before any major change in her life. After confessing her fear of the unknown to God, her allergies cleared up!

The solution to fear of the unknown is to make sure that you love God and are following His calling for your life. Based on this, He promises that all things will work together for your good and that He will never leave you![15]

3. Fear of Failure

Many men are controlled by this fear. They will sacrifice their marriages and relationships with their children in order to succeed in their jobs. God gives a clear remedy for this—if you meditate on His Word day and night, whatever you do will prosper.[16]

A certain doctor began to memorize and meditate on Scripture while he was in college. His grades rose until he was in the top ten percent of his class. Upon completion of his medical residency training, he was one of the top resident physicians in the nation and received the Resident Teaching Award.

An attorney has experienced remarkable success in the legal profession as he has memorized the entire New Testament and much of the Old Testament.

4. Fear of Poverty

This fear causes many to develop the love of money. It is based on trusting our own abilities and resources to meet our needs and on a false perception of prosperity. The solution to this fear is to dedicate all your resources to God, choose to be a "seed sower," and learn to be content with food and clothing.

5. Fear of Sickness and Death

Jesus died to deliver us from this fear. He calls us to enter into freedom by choosing to lay down our lives for Him and others.[17]

God identifies three categories of fears.

1. **Reverential Fear of God**
   This is vital for every person.
2. **Fear of Danger**
   This fear is for our safety.
3. **Fears From Satan's Lies**
   These are always damaging and must be cast out.

Angie and Abigail tried various remedies to clear their complexions. One day, they learned that their condition may be due to the stress of fear, which can trigger hormonal imbalances.

They confessed their fears to the Lord, and shortly thereafter, there was such a noticeable improvement that other people commented about it. Their improvement continued as long as they overcame fear and all its associated stresses.

Seven Commands to Conquer Fear

1. Follow Me

"Follow me, and I will make you fishers of men."[18]

Resulting Quality: Meekness

No matter how many dangers lurk in the shadows, sheep have no fear as long as they stay close to their shepherd. This is David's testimony: "Yea, though I walk through the valley of the shadow of death, I will fear no evil: for thou art with me."[19]

The greatest danger that sheep face is allowing themselves to be drawn away from their shepherd by their own appetites. They will then be vulnerable to marauding wolves, lions, bears, and thieves.

Similarly, "every man is tempted, when he is drawn away of his own lust, and enticed. Then when lust hath conceived, it bringeth forth sin: and sin, when it is finished, bringeth forth death."[20]

Great visions bring great courage.

Gideon was a fearful man until he received a verbal blessing: "The LORD is with thee, thou mighty man of valor."[21] That blessing came true, and Gideon was given the vision to deliver his nation from the iron rule of their enemies.

In this command, Jesus gives us a similar verbal blessing and vision for a great work: "Follow me, and I will make you fishers of men." Our vision should be to draw as many people as we can to the love and power of the Lord Jesus Christ. In so doing, we will fulfill the promise that God gave Abraham: "In thee and in thy seed shall all the families of the earth be blessed."[22]

This will be the ultimate result of following Jesus and having Him make us fishers of men. For this great work, Jesus will never leave us: "Go ye therefore, and teach all nations . . . to observe all things whatsoever I have commanded you: and, lo, I am with you always, even unto the end of the world."[23]

Personal Application

- ☐ How closely would Jesus say that I am following Him in my life?
- ☐ What wrong desires draw me away from the Lord and cause me to have fears and doubts?
- ☐ Do I understand that God's purpose for my life is to bring as many as I can to Christ and to disciple them with His commands?
- ☐ Have I embraced this calling and received a blessing to carry it out?

Fear is the natural consequence of straying from the Shepherd.

Courtesy of www.SolveFamilyProblems.com

Gideon was a fearful man until he received a verbal blessing and a vision for a great work.

Fear is cast out by love when we embrace our God-given call of drawing multitudes to the power of Christ's love and truth.

2. Take My Yoke

"Take my yoke upon you, and learn of me . . . .
For my yoke is easy, and my burden is light."[24]

Resulting Quality: **Obedience**

Jewish boys were expected to memorize the Torah, which contains the five books of Moses. At the age of thirteen, they passed from childhood to adulthood with a ceremony called a bar mitzvah, which means "son of the law."[25]

They continued to memorize the Scriptures, and at the age of fifteen they were allowed to choose which of the two rabbinical schools they wanted to join: the school of Hillel or the school of Schammai.[26] Each school added a burdensome load of requirements, regulations, and traditions to the Law, which in many ways voided the commands of God. This was the case with the command to honor fathers and mothers, which they got around by dedicating all their money to God as "Corban."[27]

When a young man was inducted into a rabbinical school, it was said of him that he took on its "yoke," which meant that he placed himself under the burden of all their rules, regulations, and traditions.

Jesus' yoke is light and easy.

To the weary and discouraged followers of man-made religions, Jesus gives a refreshing invitation: "Come unto me, all ye that labor and are heavy laden, and I will give you rest. Take my yoke upon you, and learn of me; for I am meek and lowly in heart: and ye shall find rest unto your souls. For my yoke is easy, and my burden is light."[28]

The rabbinical systems were burdensome, but so was the Law of Moses because of the law of sin in the flesh. Therefore, Paul said, "The commandment, which was ordained to life, I found to be unto death."[29] The yoke that Jesus gives comprises His commands, and they are light and easy because He gives us the power of His Holy Spirit to carry them out. "For this is the love of God, that we keep his commandments: and his commandments are not grievous."[30]

Personal Application

- ☐ Have I embraced the yoke of Jesus by which I will learn His heart and nature?
- ☐ Have I had the elders of my church lay hands on me for an effective life ministry?
- ☐ Do I daily ask for the filling of the Holy Spirit and the grace I need to carry Christ's yoke?
- ☐ Do I understand that with these provisions I am under God's protection, provision, and direction?

The yoke of the Pharisees was the burdensome religious system that they required all their followers to carry out to the letter.

The Torah consists of the five books of Moses. It is a "schoolmaster" to bring us to Christ.

The word translated *schoolmaster* is *paidagōgós,* from which we get the word *pedagogue.* Wealthy families hired a *paidagōgós* to be a strict disciplinarian for a son until he reached maturity and was then able to live by the rules he had learned.

Failure to keep the Law was atoned by animal sacrifices until Christ became the Lamb of God and paid the full penalty for all sin.[31]

Wisdom resolves fear. What we do not understand we tend to fear, and what we fear we tend to worship. This can be seen among those who fear global warming, who tend to worship the earth.

Ravenous wolves are great motivations to stay close to our wise Shepherd.

Snakes sense danger with their tongues and avoid confrontation when possible.

3. Be Wise as Serpents

"Behold, I send you forth as sheep in the midst of wolves: be ye therefore wise as serpents, and harmless as doves."[32]

Resulting Quality: Wisdom

The best way to be wise is to walk with those who are wise: "He that walketh with wise men shall be wise: but a companion of fools shall be destroyed."[33] The need for wisdom is obvious if we are in the midst of a pack of ravenous wolves. This makes it imperative that we follow our wise Shepherd—very closely!

God has a purpose for placing us among wolves.

Why would Jesus send His defenseless sheep among ravenous wolves? If it were simply a matter of the sheep being torn apart by the wolves, there would be no reason to instruct the sheep to be wise. God's purpose for this strategy is to disable the wolves so that they will not be able to continue to damage the flock of God.

God could instantly destroy all the wolves without the help of the sheep. However, He delights to use that which is weak to confound the mighty and that which the world calls foolish to confound man's wisdom. Paul affirms this: "For ye see your calling, brethren, how that not many wise men after the flesh, not many mighty, not many noble, are called: But God hath chosen the foolish things of the world to confound the wise; and God hath chosen the weak things of the world to confound the things which are mighty . . . That no flesh should glory in his presence."[34]

We can conquer through death.

The most powerful people on the face of the earth are those who have no fear of death. Therefore, when we embrace the prospect of laying down our lives in order to bring life to many others, we lose our fear of death! The Book of Revelation states that the believers "overcame him [Satan] by the blood of the Lamb, and by the word of their testimony; and they loved not their lives unto the death."[35]

Personal Application

- ☐ If I am a disciple of the Lord Jesus Christ, then He has sent me out to be among wolves. Can I recognize them?
- ☐ God warns us that the devil walks about every day as a roaring lion seeking whom he may destroy.[36] Am I hearing his roar in my life?
- ☐ Do I anticipate dangerous situations and plan out wise ways to avoid them or respond to them?
- ☐ Have I purposed to lay down my life to serve the Lord and take the good news of His Gospel to many other nations?

4. Be a House of Prayer

"My house shall be called of all nations the house of prayer."[37]

Resulting Quality: **Persuasiveness**

Satan trembles when wise believers pray with power. Such prayer does great damage to his destructive work among believers and non-believers alike. His objective is to torment believers by striking fear in our hearts. We know that fear is from Satan, because "God hath not given us the spirit of fear; but of power, and of love, and of a sound mind."[38]

Dedicate your body as a house of prayer.

In order to follow this command, you must realize that your body is the temple of the Lord: "Know ye not that your body is the temple of the Holy Ghost which is in you?"[39]

Just as Solomon dedicated the Temple with sacrifices to be a house of prayer, so God wants us to dedicate our bodies to be living sacrifices to carry out the functions of powerful prayer.[40]

Cleanse your house of prayer.

The illicit activities that Jesus cleansed from the Temple had damaged its role as a house of prayer.[41] Similarly, we must cleanse our lives of anything that would damage our fervent, effectual prayer. This is why we are told, "Be not conformed to this world: but be ye transformed by the renewing of your mind, that ye may prove what is that good, and acceptable, and perfect, will of God."[42]

Learn to pray with power.

God gives supernatural answers to prayer when we cry out to Him with our voices, believe in our hearts that He will answer, and make requests that are consistent with His name and His Word. God promises, "Call unto me, and I will answer thee, and show thee great and mighty things, which thou knowest not,"[43] and "Call upon me in the day of trouble: I will deliver thee, and thou shalt glorify me."[44] Jesus said that His house of prayer should be for all nations, not just for our little circles of friends.

Personal Application

- ☐ Have I dedicated my body to God as a living sacrifice to be a house of prayer and to serve His kingdom?
- ☐ Have I cleansed my life of everything that would grieve the Holy Spirit and quench His power in and through my life?
- ☐ Do I understand that the power of one-accord prayer requires that I love God with all my heart, soul, mind, and strength?
- ☐ Have I ever experienced supernatural results by crying out to God for a humanly impossible situation?

A house of prayer must be a house of power. This comes by being of one accord, which involves loving the Lord with all our hearts, souls, minds, and strength.[45]

Hundreds are experiencing the supernatural results of one-accord prayer.

Miguel and Ada desperately desired a child. After years of no results, a large group cried out with one accord for them, and their first child was soon conceived.

After five more years, they again asked a group of one-accord believers to cry out for them, and their second child was conceived.

5. Receive God's Power

"Tarry ye in the city of Jerusalem, until ye be endued with power from on high."[46]

Resulting Quality: **Orderliness**

The power of God's Spirit and the love that He perfects in our hearts can cast out fears. "There is no fear in love; but perfect love casteth out fear: because fear hath torment. He that feareth is not made perfect in love."[47]

Receive God's Spirit.

When you were born again by confessing with your mouth Jesus as Lord and believing in your heart that God raised Him from the dead, the Holy Spirit united with your spirit, and you were given the ability to have fellowship with Him.[48] That is the first step toward experiencing the power of God.

Be filled with God's Spirit.

The Holy Spirit is a Person of the Trinity. When you were born again, you got all of the Holy Spirit. However, He did not get all of you, because you have three parts: spirit, soul, and body.[49] You need a daily filling of the Holy Spirit in your soul after you are born again in your spirit.

Jesus explains how this happens: "If a son shall ask bread of any of you that is a father, will he give him a stone? . . . If ye then, being evil, know how to give good gifts unto your children: how much more shall your heavenly Father give the Holy Spirit to them that ask him?"[50]

Since asking for bread is a daily experience, you should begin each day by asking God to fill your soul with His Spirit along with wisdom and grace. In this way, you follow the command to "be filled with the Spirit."[51] The verb tense in this verse indicates a present, continuous action, which means that you must keep on being filled.

Experience the power of God's Spirit.

Jesus went to the wilderness with the filling of the Spirit, but He returned in the power of the Spirit. We also must be tested in order to experience the power of God's Spirit.[52]

Personal Application

- ☐ Have I received the Holy Spirit in my spirit by being born again?
- ☐ Do I ask my heavenly Father each day to fill my soul with His Holy Spirit, His wisdom, and the power of His grace?
- ☐ Do I anticipate trials and temptations and welcome them as the means by which I will grow in grace and in God's power?
- ☐ Do I overcome each temptation with God's Spirit and Word?

We are born again by God's Spirit and the living seed of God's Word.[53]

We grow by the grace of God and the knowledge of the Lord Jesus Christ through His Word.[54]

We come to maturity by going through trials and tribulations, which produce patience, hope, and the power of God's love.[55]

6. Watch and Pray

"Watch and pray, that ye enter not into temptation."[56]

Resulting Quality: Endurance

Fear is the result of failing to watch and pray. We must watch because our adversary, the devil, walks about as a roaring lion, seeking whom he may devour. We are to resist him steadfastly with faith and the rhemas of Scripture, knowing that the same afflictions are taking place in the lives of our Christian brothers.[57]

We can be certain that Satan is stalking every believer and will destroy the weakest ones.

Thus we must watch that our love for Christ never grows cold.

What are we to watch for?

The most important condition to keep your eye on is the level of love that you have for the Lord Jesus Christ. If you have lost your love, you will be vulnerable to Satan's attack, and the potential for great works will be destroyed. You must carefully search out and destroy anything that damages your love for the Lord.

The Laodicean church is a prime example of a group of believers who lost their love for Jesus Christ. The result was a lukewarm spiritual condition, which is nauseating to God. They were spiritually impotent, yet they believed that they were doing well. They said that they were rich and had need of nothing, when actually they were poor, wretched, and miserable.[58]

What are we to pray for?

Jesus taught us to pray, "Lead us not into temptation, but deliver us from evil."[59] Peter failed to watch and pray in the garden. As a result, he was drawn into the temptation to deny Jesus, and he failed the test.

It is easy to overlook approaching danger. Therefore, we need the help of fellow believers to "exhort one another daily, while it is called Today; lest any of you be hardened through the deceitfulness of sin."[60]

Courtesy of www.SolveFamilyProblems.com

Jesus knew that Peter would be tempted to deny Him and fail three times.

Therefore, He told him to watch and pray so that he would not enter into temptation.

Personal Application

- ☐ Have I left my first love, as would be indicated by a lack of desire to spend time in God's Word and in prayer?
- ☐ How would Jesus evaluate my level of love for Him right now?
- ☐ Since Satan walks about as a roaring lion, what is the most vulnerable area of my life that he is likely to attack?
- ☐ What trusted friends have I asked to also watch for areas in my life that are open to Satan's attack?

7. Fear Not

"Fear not them which kill the body, but are not able to kill the soul."[61]

Resulting Quality: Boldness

For most people, death is the ultimate fear. Yet it is this very fear that Jesus died to overcome, "that through death he might destroy him that had the power of death, that is, the devil; And deliver them who through fear of death were all their lifetime subject to bondage."[62]

Nearly one-third of the billions of dollars of Medicare expenditures for the elderly are spent during the last year of life.[63,64,65] The goal of extending life just a little bit longer is often based on an inner fear of dying. The believer knows that he is indestructible until his work on earth is done.

Have hope for life beyond the grave.

As a believer, you have a glorious hope after your life on this earth comes to an end. You will enjoy the presence of the Lord in the splendor of heaven. When Dr. Josef Tson was told that he would be killed if he did not renounce the Lord, he calmly replied with a smile: "Don't you understand that when you kill me you send me to glory? You cannot threaten me with glory!"[66] Because of this confidence, you should not sorrow "as others which have no hope."[67]

Have a passion for life before the grave.

The purpose for your life is to carry out the great works that God designed you to accomplish.[68] These involve leading as many people as you can to the love and truth of the Lord Jesus Christ and then discipling them in His commands. This should be the passion of your life and the purpose of your death.

This was the outlook that Paul had. His passion was to reach the Gentile world with the powerful Gospel of Christ.[69] When he faced death, he wanted to depart and be with the Lord, but he knew that his work was not yet finished, so he determined to remain.[70]

Personal Application

- ☐ **Do I have the confidence that if I were to die right now, I would immediately be with the Lord in heaven?**
- ☐ **When I meet the Lord, and He asks me how many people I have discipled, what will I tell Him?**
- ☐ **Have I chosen to lay down my life in serving the Lord, and do I realize that I am indestructible until my work is done?**
- ☐ **Paul asked fellow believers to pray for him to have boldness. Have I asked my friends to pray for me to have boldness?**

John Wesley recognized the power of overcoming fear.

"Give me one hundred preachers, who fear nothing but sin, and desire nothing but God, and I care not whether they be clergymen or laymen, they alone will shake the gates of hell and set up the kingdom of heaven upon earth."[71]

—John Wesley

During the rule of Communist Romanian dictator Ceausescu, Dr. Josef Tson was arrested for preaching the Gospel. When his captors threatened him with death, he smiled and said: "You should know your supreme weapon is killing. My supreme weapon is dying.

"You know that my sermons are on tape all over the country. When you shoot me, you only sprinkle my sermons with my blood. Sir, my sermons will speak ten times louder after you kill me. Go on and do it!" His captors exclaimed: "Absolutely not! We could not let this happen!"[72]

Envy

How we deny or reveal envy

**"I do not envy;
I just wish . . ."**

"My husband were like . . ."
"My wife were like . . ."
"I had a family like . . ."
"My house were like . . ."
"My children were like . . ."
"My body were like . . ."
"My job were like . . ."
"I had money like . . ."

Ways we reveal envy

Comparing ourselves with others
Focusing on the things of others
Failing to enjoy what God has given
Excessive window shopping
Imagining life as someone else
Discontentment with possessions
Addiction to love novels
Putting others down
Wanting things others have

How to Resolve

Envy

Required Command	Resulting Quality
Do Unto Others Matthew 7:12	**Sensitivity** vs. Callousness
Keep My Commandments John 14:15	**Diligence** vs. Slothfulness
Feed My Sheep John 21:15–16	**Dependability** vs. Inconsistency
Baptize Believers Matthew 28:19	**Cautiousness** vs. Rashness
Make Disciples Matthew 28:20	**Flexibility** vs. Resistance
Do Not Cast Pearls Matthew 7:6	**Discretion** vs. Simplemindedness
Pray for Laborers Matthew 9:37–38	**Compassion** vs. Indifference

How Does Envy Affect the Musculoskeletal System?

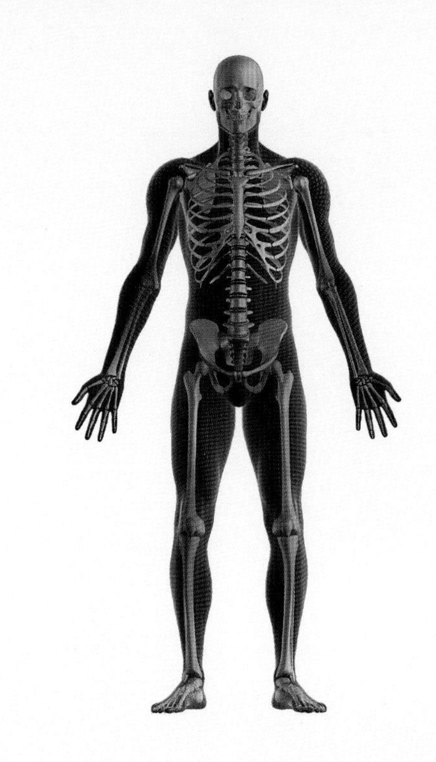

The musculoskeletal system includes bones, muscles, joints, and connective tissues such as ligaments and tendons. They make up the structure that supports the body.

Muscles are the places of greatest energy production in the body. They contain reserve stores of glycogen, an energy source used when under stress. Muscular wasting and weakness are well-known side effects of stress-induced hormones such as cortisol and antidiuretic hormone.[1]

The bones are under constant reconstruction due to the activity of cells that lay down fibrous material (osteoblasts) and other cells that take up minerals for other purposes (osteoclasts).[2] One purpose of taking up minerals, especially calcium and potassium, is to help maintain a healthy blood pH.[3]

Prevalence of Bone Disorders

An imbalance between osteoblasts and osteoclasts results in weakening and bone loss. This is called osteoporosis.

In the United States today, osteoporosis is a major health risk for 28 million people. Ten million individuals have this disease, and 18 million more have low bone mass, which places them at increased risk to develop it. Overall, approximately 8 million women and 2 million men in America have osteoporosis.[4]

The Significance of Osteoporosis in Women

The fact that so many more women than men have osteoporosis is interesting to note. Scripture states that envy is "the rottenness of the bones,"[5] and women tend to have a greater problem with envy than men.

This may be because God designed the husband to provide leadership, financial resources, discernment for wise decisions, and courage for protection. When men fail to provide these essentials, their wives tend to envy other women whose husbands do.

The Seriousness of Envy

Even though envy is the last stress in this list, it is in many ways the most vicious of all. Solomon points out, "Wrath is cruel, and anger is outrageous; but who is able to stand before envy?"[6] This is seen throughout Scripture. It was envy that caused Joseph's brothers to sell him as a slave.[7] It was envy that motivated the Pharisees to crucify Jesus.[8]

All together, the hands and feet contain 106 bones—more than half the bones in the body.[9]

As osteoporosis develops and calcium is leached out of the bones, they become full of tiny holes, much like swiss cheese.[10]

Courtesy of www.SolveFamilyProblems.com

Envy was the motivation that caused Joseph's brothers to sell him as a slave to Ishmaelite traders for twenty pieces of silver.[19]

Courtesy of www.SolveFamilyProblems.com

Joseph's dreams of his brothers bowing down to him were a present reality to them. We tend to be controlled by the ones we envy.

Envy affects our daily thinking, appetite, emotions, health, and relationships with God and others.

"Let not thine heart envy sinners: but be thou in the fear of the LORD all the day long. For surely there is an end; and thine expectation shall not be cut off."[20]

Envy is setting your affection on what someone else has and focusing on what it takes to claim that for ourselves.

How Envy Damages Bones

Osteoporosis is a condition of bone deterioration. As calcium and other minerals are taken from the bones, holes develop, making the bones more porous.

This condition is described in the roots of the term *osteoporosis: osteon,* which means "bone"; *poros,* which means "passage"; and *osis,* which means "condition."[11] The greater the number of openings or holes in the bones, the more fragile and weak they are.

Notice how Scripture defines this condition: "My life is spent with grief, and my years with sighing: my strength faileth because of mine iniquity, and my bones are consumed."[12]

The Hebrew word for *consumed* is a precise description of osteoporosis. It means "to shrink." This explains why approximately 1.6 million hip fractures occur worldwide in osteoporosis patients each year.

One of the most significant physical consequences of envy is a deterioration of the bones. Scripture makes this very clear: "A sound heart is the life of the flesh: but envy the rottenness of the bones."[13] The Hebrew word for *rottenness* means "decay." This is another precise description of osteoporosis.

When Calcium Is Ineffective

When osteoporosis patients are given their diagnoses, they assume that if they take calcium supplements or pharmaceutical drugs, the condition will be remedied. However, if they have the stress of envy, there will be a high cortisol level, which will offset the benefit of calcium and any pharmaceuticals.

Renowned researcher and lecturer David Zava, Ph.D., explains this important point: "Calcium supplementation and alendronate-type drugs used to inhibit bone resorption . . . will always fight a losing battle to high cortisol. I frequently see women reporting continued bone loss, despite use of pharmaceutical bone resorption inhibitors, when salivary cortisol levels are very high."[14]

Rather than fighting osteoporosis, excess calcium and vitamins may complicate the problem and produce constipation or kidney stones.[15,16]

The Health of the Body

In the center of the bones is the marrow, where stem cells produce red blood cells. Therefore, the health of the marrow determines the health of the body since the "the life of all flesh is the blood."[17]

God promises that if you follow His ways, you will have strong bones and healthy marrow; but if you violate His ways, you will experience the decay and deterioration of your bones. Scripture states: "Be not wise in thine own eyes: fear the LORD, and depart from evil. It shall be health to thy navel, and marrow to thy bones."[18]

How to Conquer Envy With Sincere Gratefulness

Envy is the rottenness of the heart as well as the bones. Thus to overcome envy is to undergo a heart change. You must first recognize how envy has depleted your heart of love for God and others and then take Biblical steps to resolve this heart condition.

Identify the subject of envy.

Envy is directed toward individuals. It focuses on people who have talents, abilities, attributes, or things that you feel you must have in order to be happy or receive approval and recognition. Envy produces competition. When an envious person hears others praised, he experiences inward pain and resentment, which only deepens his envy.

Choose to make others successful.

Envy is born out of a desire for greatness and for the approval that comes from doing great works. Jesus never condemned the desire to be great; He just tells us that the way to get there is to serve others. The more people who allow you to serve them, the greater you will be.

For example, a mayor serves all the people in his city, a governor serves all the people in his state, and a president serves all the people in his nation. This is the basis of Christ's teaching that "whosoever will be chief among you, let him be your servant."[21]

Timothy was a great man. His greatness did not come by envying other disciples but by developing a servant's spirit. Thus Paul said of him: "I have no man likeminded, who will naturally care for your state. For all seek their own, not the things which are Jesus Christ's."[22]

Discover the secret of dying to self.

The goal to become great is honorable if you want to be great for God and His kingdom. However, it is destructive if your goal is simply to exalt yourself or your ambitions. Doing great things for God requires that you first die to your own wants and desires and then ask God for the grace, wisdom, and resources to be effective for Him and His kingdom.

Learn the skill of praise.

The very praise that you desire is also longed for by others. It is hard to envy someone you have sincerely praised. "Be kindly affectioned one to another with brotherly love; in honor preferring one another."[23]

Realize what people really admire.

An envious person thinks that other people admire talent, possessions, appearance, skills, or abilities, when actually what people admire most is a genuine sense of love, compassion, kindness, loyalty, enthusiasm, and other character qualities.

Courtesy of www.SolveFamilyProblems.com

Moses discovered the secret of conquering envy when he threw down his rod.

The rod of Moses represented his profession, resources, skills, position, reputation, and every other aspect of his life.

When God told him to throw it down, it became a poisonous snake from which he fled. Whatever we grasp has the potential to bite us with poisonous venom.

When Moses picked up the rod at God's direction, it suddenly became the rod of God through which He did many miracles.[24]

Courtesy of www.SolveFamilyProblems.com

What Moses surrendered was the means of making him great.

Courtesy of www.SolveFamilyProblems.com

Haman was forced to carry out this command in a way he never expected.

King Ahasuarus asked Haman for advice on how to reward a special person. Haman thought he was the special person, so he listed the highest honors that could be given. Then the king said, "Go quickly and do this for Mordecai"—the man Haman hated and planned to kill![27]

Every person has a deep longing for praise. Effective praise involves three steps.

1. **Identify a character quality.** *("Thank you for your patience.")*
2. **Explain how it was shown.** *("You waited cheerfully for an hour.")*
3. **Tell how it encouraged you.** *("You motivated me to be patient.")*

Seven Commands to Conquer Envy

1. Do Unto Others

"All things whatsoever ye would that men should do to you, do ye even so to them."[25]

Resulting Quality: **Sensitivity**

Envy will not survive when this one command is fully lived out! This command is actually the antithesis of envy. It focuses on benefiting the lives of others with the same things that we want from them.

Just as envy is the ultimate stress, so this command is the ultimate fulfillment of God's Law: "for this is the law and the prophets."[26]

What do you want done to you?

There is a built-in strategy to carry out this command. Just make a list of what you want from other people, and then do it for them. The list will no doubt include manifestations of genuine love such as acceptance, honor, respect, approval, encouragement, and support.

These can be expressed by giving the following things to those whom you would be inclined to envy. As you give them, you will be investing in their lives, and your heart will follow your treasure.

1. **A warm, loving smile**
2. **Precise words of praise**
3. **Verbal blessings**
4. **Words of encouragement**
5. **Written notes of praise**
6. **Fervent prayer for their requests**
7. **A listening heart and ear**
8. **Good reports to others about them**
9. **Recognition of their anniversaries**
10. **Words of comfort during sorrow**

These ten items cost no money. However, they require something more valuable than money—genuine attention to their needs rather than a selfish focus on your wants. This is the essence of carrying out this command as well as the entire Law and the prophets.

Personal Application

- ☐ Do I tend to desire things that other people have, such as friends, recognition, approval, admiration, respect, and honor?
- ☐ How could I give these things to one I envy: be a friend to him, recognize his achievements, praise his character, etc.?
- ☐ When I do these things, will I realize that I am doing them because of my love for Jesus and His love for others?
- ☐ Will I remember that I should first serve those closest to me?

2. Keep My Commandments

"If ye love me, keep my commandments."[28]

Resulting Quality: Diligence

The commands that Jesus taught His disciples are forty-nine practical ways to love God and love one another. They are the heart of the kingdom message and the central truths of the entire Bible.

We all need a change of heart.

Envy is a disease of the heart. It can be conquered only by a transformed outlook on life. The Law of Moses was to be carried out as an expression of loving God. However, the emphasis was on carrying it out no matter how a person felt on the inside.

For example, the requirements of the Law had to be carried out regardless of the emotions, ideas, or will of the person doing them. However, the commands of Christ go right to the heart of a person. Clear examples are the Old Testament commands not to commit adultery or kill and Christ's commandments not to lust or be angry.[29]

In order to carry out Christ's commands, you must be given an extra measure of God's grace, which is the desire and power to do His will. John therefore states, "The law was given by Moses, but grace and truth came by Jesus Christ."[30]

Know what it means to keep Christ's commands.

Scripture makes a distinction between keeping commands and doing them: "The statutes and judgments which I speak . . . keep and do them."[31] The word Jesus used for *keep* in the Greek is *tereo*. It means "to guard from loss or injury by keeping the eye upon." An illustration would be a police officer keeping careful guard over those who are placed under his protection.

Another illustration is the navigator of a sailing ship. He charted his course by keeping his eye on the stars. This is the same concept that Jesus used when He told His disciples to keep His commands. They are fixed "lights" that can be trusted to guide us through the storms of life.

Personal Application

- ☐ Have I purposed in my heart to keep Christ's commands as a demonstration of my love for Him?
- ☐ Do I realize that the best way to keep Christ's commands before my "eyes" is to put them in my heart by memorization and meditation?
- ☐ When I have a decision to make regarding the course of my life, do I check out the commands of Christ for precise guidance?
- ☐ Does my life confirm that I am keeping Christ's commands?

A worker may have wrong attitudes in a job. However, a believer cannot have wrong attitudes and still keep Christ's commands.

The commands of Christ are like the stars of heaven by which we navigate through the storms of life.

Navigation requires training. So does keeping Christ's commands.

3. Feed My Sheep

"Lovest thou me? . . . Feed my sheep."[32]

Resulting Quality: **Dependability**

Feeding sheep requires totally giving of yourself, which is the opposite of envy.

"The good shepherd giveth his life for the sheep."[37]

After defeating Satan in the wilderness, Jesus began His public ministry by speaking with authority and casting out unclean spirits.

Courtesy of www.SolveFamilyProblems.com

The entire Bible was represented on the Mount of Transfiguration, but the teaching of Jesus is to be preeminent.

Moses represents the Law; Elijah represents the prophets; Jesus represents the Gospels; and Peter, James, and John represent the epistles.

Feeding God's flock involves far more than just teaching the Bible. God rebuked the shepherds of Israel for failing to fulfill their job description: "The diseased have ye not strengthened, neither have ye healed that which was sick, neither have ye bound up that which was broken, neither have ye brought again that which was driven away, neither have ye sought that which was lost."[33]

Notice that a spiritual shepherd's care begins with the physical, emotional, and spiritual healing of God's people. Thus Jesus sent out His disciples with "power against unclean spirits, to cast them out, and to heal all manner of sickness and all manner of disease."[34]

Teach the whole counsel of God.

When believers are properly fed, they will have the same response that the two disciples had when Jesus taught them on the road to Emmaus: "Did not our heart burn within us, while he talked with us by the way, and while he opened to us the Scriptures?"[35]

How did Jesus teach them? "And beginning at Moses and all the prophets, he expounded unto them in all the Scriptures the things concerning himself."[36]

Every command of Christ in the Gospels has its roots in the testimonies, types, examples, and teachings of the Old Testament and its application in the epistles of the New Testament. When this threefold witness is properly taught along with personal examples, the hearts of listeners leap for joy. They are fed, grow strong, and reproduce.

With the command to "feed My sheep," we would first explain how David fed the nation of Israel with his Psalms then go to the application in the epistles of being filled with the Spirit and speaking in Psalms, hymns, and spiritual songs. By teaching the commands in this way, you can demonstrate your love for Jesus.

Personal Application

- ☐ Is it my goal to learn and apply the commands of Christ so that I can effectively teach them to others from firsthand experience?
- ☐ Do I know how to find Old Testament examples and New Testament applications for each command?
- ☐ When I teach Christ's commands in this way, do I speak with confidence, knowing that I am rightly dividing the Word of truth?
- ☐ Do the hearts of my listeners "burn within them" as the Holy Spirit confirms the truth and application of what I share?

4. Baptize Believers

"Go ye therefore, and teach all nations, baptizing them in the name of the Father, and of the Son, and of the Holy Ghost."[38]

Resulting Quality: **Cautiousness**

There are two primary baptisms for all believers. New believers are baptized with water to symbolize the new birth.[39] Jesus baptizes us "with the Holy Ghost, and with fire."[40]

The baptism with water represents new birth.

When three thousand repented due to the preaching of Peter, they were baptized with water. Peter compares water baptism to the days of Noah in which eight people were delivered from the floodwaters by the ark. The ark is a picture of being in Christ.

"The like figure whereunto even baptism doth also now save us (not the putting away of the filth of the flesh, but the answer of a good conscience toward God,) by the resurrection of Jesus Christ."[41]

The baptism with the Holy Ghost and fire gives us power.

On the Day of Pentecost, 120 disciples "were all with one accord in one place. . . . And there appeared unto them cloven tongues like as of fire, and it sat upon each of them. And they were all filled with the Holy Ghost."[42] We then see several instances where the Holy Spirit was given by the laying on of hands.

Those who believed on the Lord in Samaria were baptized. Then Peter and John prayed that they would receive the Holy Ghost and "laid they their hands on them, and they received the Holy Ghost."[43]

When Paul was converted, God sent Ananias to lay hands on him to restore his sight and fill him with the Holy Spirit.[44] Then he was baptized. Paul laid hands on Timothy and later wrote, "Stir up the gift of God, which is in thee by the putting on of my hands."[45]

Personal Application

- ☐ Have I been baptized as a public declaration of my faith in the Lord Jesus Christ to identify with His death, burial, and resurrection?
- ☐ Have I experienced a one-accord fellowship with other believers so that the Holy Spirit would come upon us with power?
- ☐ Have I had elders lay hands on me and pray for God to fill me with His Spirit for a more effective ministry?
- ☐ Am I aware that anointing with oil and fervent prayer by elders is a provision in the New Testament for healing?

A conquering Israelite king cleansed what he captured with water and fire, symbolizing baptism.[46]

Clay vessels are shaped with water and perfected with fire.

Courtesy of www.SolveFamilyProblems.com

The laying on of hands is foundational for believers.

The principles and foundation of the Gospel of Christ include "the doctrine of baptisms and of laying on of hands."[47]

5. Make Disciples

"Go ye therefore, and teach all nations . . . to observe all things whatsoever I have commanded you."[48]

Resulting Quality: **Flexibility**

A disciple is like a disciplined soldier. This is evidenced in his dress, music, friends, and social life.

"We must through much tribulation enter into the kingdom of God."[54]

This command is most effectively carried out when believers achieve a one-accord fellowship to disable the principalities and powers of darkness over cities and become living examples of Christ's commands.

Therefore, the final prayer of Jesus in the garden emphasizes the goal of having one accord: "That they all may be one; as thou, Father, art in me, and I in thee, that they also may be one in us: that the world may believe that thou hast sent me."[49] This all-encompassing objective leaves no room for the envy that comes from personal ambitions.

How do we make disciples?

This is an important question, because if you do not know how to make disciples, you certainly will not know what to do when you go out to minister. The answer is in the very words of this command. We make disciples by "Teaching them to observe all things" that Jesus commanded us.[50] A disciple is one who dedicates himself to learning and following all Christ's commands.

In the process of achieving this goal, Jesus will reveal Himself to the disciple, and a new relationship will be established. Jesus pointed out: "Ye are my friends, if ye do whatsoever I command you. Henceforth I call you not servants . . . but I have called you friends; for all things [commands] that I have heard of my Father I have made known unto you."[51]

Toward this goal, Jesus said: "If ye abide in me, and my words abide in you, ye shall ask what ye will, and it shall be done unto you. Herein is my Father glorified, that ye bear much fruit; so shall ye be my disciples."[52]

If just ten believers each made ten disciples every year, and their disciples did the same, the entire world would be discipled within ten years.

How do we make "disciple makers"?

A faithful disciple does not only observe all Christ's commands but also teaches them to others so that they, in turn, can make more disciples. Therefore, Paul instructed his disciple, Timothy, "The things that thou hast heard of me among many witnesses, the same commit thou to faithful men, who shall be able to teach others also."[53]

Personal Application

- ☐ Have I learned the commands of Christ?
- ☐ Am I applying them to my life on a daily basis?
- ☐ Am I teaching others the rich truths that I am experiencing?
- ☐ How many disciples am I working with at the present time?

6. Do Not Cast Pearls

"Give not that which is holy unto the dogs, neither cast ye your pearls before swine."[55]

Resulting Quality: Discretion

Much discretion is necessary in the process of making disciples. Not everyone is ready to be discipled. Harsh reactions can be encountered, and some people may seek to be discipled as a means of selfish gain.

Discern unresolved stresses.

Simon the sorcerer is an example of a person with wrong motives. He had "used sorcery, and bewitched the people of Samaria, giving out that himself was some great one."[56]

Simon had been converted by Philip's preaching. "When Simon saw that through laying on of the apostles' hands the Holy Ghost was given, he offered them money, Saying, Give me also this power, that on whomsoever I lay hands, he may receive the Holy Ghost."[57]

Peter sharply rebuked him because he recognized that Simon had a spirit of envy in him, along with greed, bitterness, and lust: "Thy money perish with thee . . . . Thou hast neither part nor lot in this matter: for thy heart is not right in the sight of God. . . . For I perceive that thou art in the gall of bitterness, and in the bond of iniquity."[58]

An unregenerate person has no capacity to value the pearls of God's wisdom.

Courtesy of www.SolveFamilyProblems.com

Discern unregenerate minds.

There are people who have no capacity to comprehend or apply the living truth of God's Word. They have put their minds above the Bible and the Holy Spirit, thereby making themselves fools. We are warned, "Speak not in the ears of a fool: for he will despise the wisdom of thy words."[59]

Neither are we to correct one who scorns God's ways: "He that reproveth a scorner getteth to himself shame: and he that rebuketh a wicked man getteth himself a blot. Reprove not a scorner, lest he hate thee."[60]

Peter wisely discerned that Simon had no place in ministry because of unresolved stresses in his heart.

Personal Application

- ☐ Have I ever experienced the disappointing results of trying to disciple someone who had impure motives?
- ☐ Have I tried to explain God's wisdom to one who misunderstood it and ridiculed me for it?
- ☐ Have I ever tried to correct scorners and felt the bitter reaction of their hatred toward me?
- ☐ Do I know how to discern unresolved stresses in a person and give them answers from the commands of Christ?

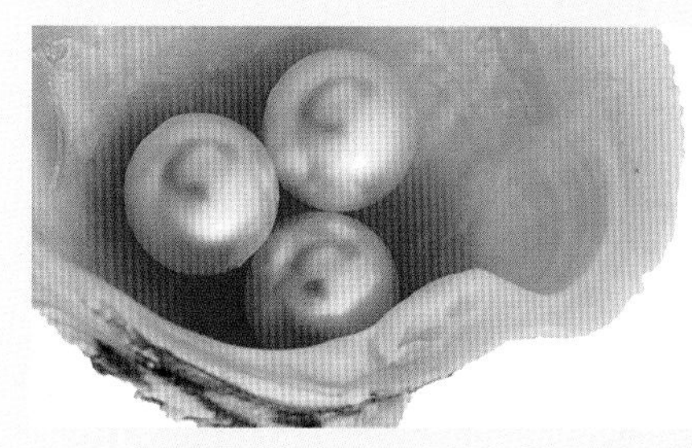

Casting a pearl before swine will anger them, because they will expect it to satisfy their appetite.

*P*rayer from a heart of compassion will produce laborers for the harvest.

*T*he fruit of our prayers will be a great harvest of redeemed souls from every nation, tongue, and people.

*I*magine the joy when we meet all who have been led to Christ by our fervent prayers and diligent work in the fields of harvest!

7. Pray for Laborers

"Pray ye therefore the Lord of the harvest, that he will send forth laborers into his harvest."[61]

Resulting Quality: Compassion

The ultimate victory over envy is to be trained, experienced, and equipped to bring Christ's love and truth to a lost, dying world. This task is far bigger than we can ever accomplish with our own strength or resources.

Only when we see multitudes of people through a heart of compassion will we be motivated to pray fervently for laborers.

Who is the Lord the harvest?

Based on the instruction of Jesus, we are to ask the Father for all our requests in Jesus' name.[62] Therefore, our prayers for laborers should be to our heavenly Father. Jesus states that He also sends forth laborers—He said, "I send you forth."[63] It was the Holy Ghost Who directed the elders in the church in Antioch to send out Paul and Barnabas for the ministry He had called them to.[64] Therefore, all three Persons of the Trinity are actively involved in sending out laborers.

What is the work of laborers?

After Jesus told His disciples to pray for laborers, He called them and "gave them power against unclean spirits, to cast them out, and to heal all manner of sickness and all manner of disease."[65]

There is an important sequence in this matter of praying for laborers. First, we are to recognize that the fields are already "white unto harvest." Second, we are to have compassion on the multitudes who are in the fields, ready for harvest. Third, we are to go and reach the multitudes.

Why is there urgency in this prayer?

Often a nation will have a window of opportunity to be discipled, and then the door will be closed for many years. To procrastinate is to miss the opportunity: "Say not ye, There are yet four months, and then cometh harvest? behold, I say unto you, Lift up your eyes, and look on the fields; for they are white already to harvest."[66]

Personal Application

- ☐ Do I have compassion when I see multitudes of people?
- ☐ Have I fervently prayed that the Lord of the harvest will send out laborers into His harvest?
- ☐ Am I ready to be sent out by the Holy Spirit to give the commands of Christ to all those I meet?

The Secret to Renewing Your Strength

The Promise

At various times, we all need to renew our strength. Some need it occasionally, while others have chronic fatigue and take months to recover. Yet God has told us how to renew our strength. It is by waiting on the Lord. But what does this involve, and how do we do it?

"[God] giveth power to the faint; and to them that have no might he increaseth strength. Even the youths shall faint and be weary, and the young men shall utterly fall: But they that wait upon the LORD shall renew their strength; they shall mount up with wings as eagles; they shall run, and not be weary; and they shall walk, and not faint."[1]

Key Questions

What Is Waiting on the Lord?

Waiting on the Lord is not a passive state of existence but an active exercise of the spirit controlling the soul. To wait on the Lord is to bring together the three functions of the soul so that they are in harmony with one another and the will of God.

What Causes Energy Loss?

Energy is lost through the stress of a divided soul. This means that the intellect is competing with the emotions or with the will. This creates a double-minded condition, and Scripture warns that "A double minded man is unstable in all his ways."[2]

What is the Root Cause of Stress?

The underlying cause of stress and conflict of the soul is expectations. When you have expectations of anyone or anything other than God, you will experience the stress of disillusionment, disappointment, and discouragement.

This is why Scripture gives the following instruction: "My soul, wait thou only upon God; for my expectation is from him."[3]

A prime example of stress from expectations is given in the account of Mary and Martha. Martha was busy, working for Jesus, but Mary was delighted to wait on the Lord. Martha had expectations of Mary's help, and when it did not come, she reacted by scolding Jesus for not instructing Mary to help her.

Expectations are based on getting what you need or want from

"They that wait upon the LORD shall renew their strength; they shall mount up with wings as eagles; they shall run, and not be weary; and they shall walk, and not faint."[4]

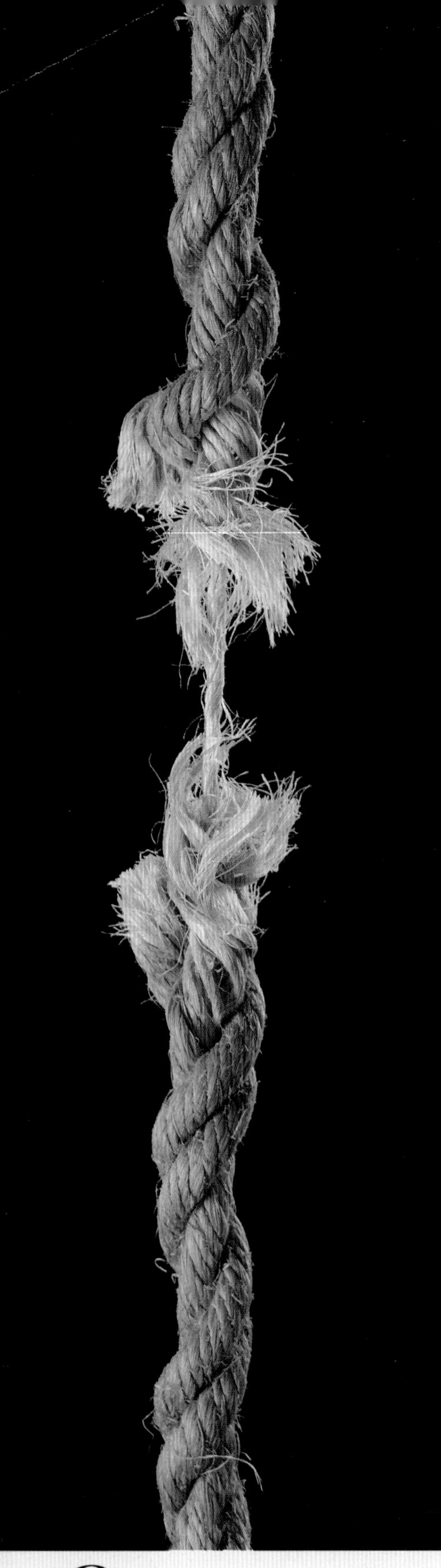

Expectations turn into rights and create stress when we look to people for what only God can do, thus making them our idols.

others. Waiting on the Lord is looking forward to receiving from Him all that you need for a successful life.

What Is the Difference Between Pressure and Stress?

The stress from expectations and a divided soul must be distinguished from the pressures of daily responsibilities. God-given pressure can be beneficial in motivating you to draw on the grace of God and achieve great works for Him. Stress from a divided soul robs you of energy so that you do not have the desire or power to carry out great works.

Paul had great pressures from work, but he was stress-free after he learned that God's strength was perfected in his weakness. Then he testified, "I labored more abundantly than they all: yet not I, but the grace of God which was with me."[5] When stress is added to pressures, or when God's grace is resisted, your human energy will be quickly drained.

What Happens When Expectations Become Rights?

By focusing on expectations, you soon turn them into personal rights to which you believe you are entitled. These rights are not only damaging to your soul, but they are totally contrary to the nature of Jesus.

"Come unto me, all ye that labor and are heavy laden, and I will give you rest. Take my yoke upon you, and learn of me; for I am meek and lowly in heart: and ye shall find rest unto your souls. For my yoke is easy, and my burden is light."[6]

Jesus laid aside all His rights and took the form of a servant, even to the point of death.

How Can I Resolve Stress?

Stress can be resolved as you discern the expectations and rights that are dividing your soul and yield them to God. This is the key to meekness, which gives you rest in your soul. When expectations are removed, your heart is strengthened, as Scripture promises: "Wait on the LORD: be of good courage, and he shall strengthen thine heart: wait, I say, on the LORD."[7]

What Does It Mean to Wait?

The root of the word for *wait* in Hebrew is *qâwâh*. It means "to bind together, to collect, to be joined together." When this word is attached to the functions of the soul, it suddenly takes on significant meaning—that of weaving together the intellect, will, and emotions.

The first mention of the Hebrew word *qâwâh* is in Genesis 1:9: "Let the waters of the heaven be gathered [*qâwâh*] together unto one place." Just as God gathered the waters together in His creation, so He wants us to collect the elements of our souls together under the authority of His Word and His Spirit.

How Can I Detect a Divided Soul?

God will reveal a divided soul as you come before Him and patiently wait for Him. While you are waiting for Him to search your soul, you can listen to Him by reading His word.

"I wait for the LORD, my soul doth wait, and in his word do I hope. My soul waiteth for the LORD more than they that watch for the morning: I say, more than they that watch for the morning."[8]

Appendix

Steps to Success

1. Resolve the Stress of Basic Youth Conflicts.

In 1964, Bill Gothard was asked by his alma mater to teach a summer course on Basic Youth Conflicts. Forty-six students were enrolled in the first course. The next year, there were 120. The following year, one thousand students took the course, then ten thousand, and then fifty thousand. Before long, 350,000 people a year were attending this 32-hour seminar in response to word-of-mouth recommendations by those whose lives, marriages, and families had been transformed by what they learned.

Nearly three million youth and adults from across the nation and around the world have now completed this seminar. You can obtain a DVD set of the seminar for viewing in your home or community. Contact the Dallas Seminar Office for details at 214-421-0001 or semops@iblp.org.

2. Identify the Qualities to Resolve Your Most Pressing Stresses.

Anger	*Guilt*	*Lust*	*Bitterness*	*Greed*	*Fear*	*Envy*
☐ Humility	☐ Security	☐ Love	☐ Punctuality	☐ Generosity	☐ Meekness	☐ Sensitivity
☐ Joyfulness	☐ Enthusiasm	☐ Self-Control	☐ Determination	☐ Thriftiness	☐ Obedience	☐ Diligence
☐ Justice	☐ Attentiveness	☐ Faith	☐ Gentleness	☐ Initiative	☐ Wisdom	☐ Dependability
☐ Creativity	☐ Thoroughness	☐ Decisiveness	☐ Availability	☐ Contentment	☐ Persuasiveness	☐ Cautiousness
☐ Sincerity	☐ Responsibility	☐ Alertness	☐ Patience	☐ Hospitality	☐ Orderliness	☐ Flexibility
☐ Honor	☐ Discernment	☐ Virtue	☐ Forgiveness	☐ Resourcefulness	☐ Endurance	☐ Discretion
☐ Deference	☐ Truthfulness	☐ Loyalty	☐ Tolerance	☐ Gratefulness	☐ Boldness	☐ Compassion

3. Discover How to Live Out These Qualities.

Beautifully illustrated, *The Power for True Success* defines each quality and explains how to apply it in practical ways to your daily life.

Just knowing about character qualities is not enough of a motivation to build them into our lives. We need the power of God's grace to make it happen, and then we need practical steps of action for each character quality.

This valuable resource identifies the real essence of a character quality and traces its roots back to the wisdom of Scripture. Order from store.iblp.org.

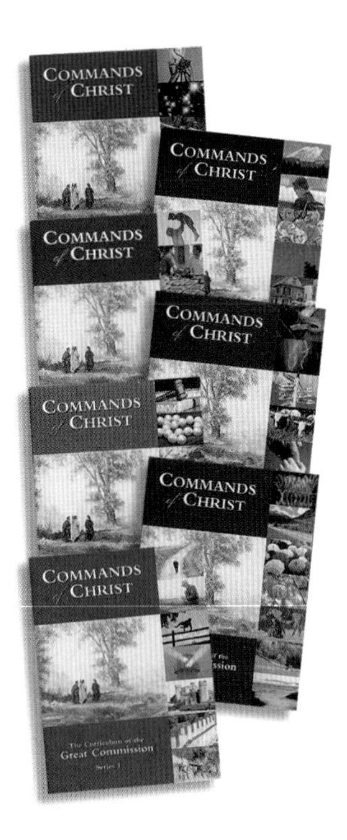

4. Discover How to Apply 49 Laws of Love.

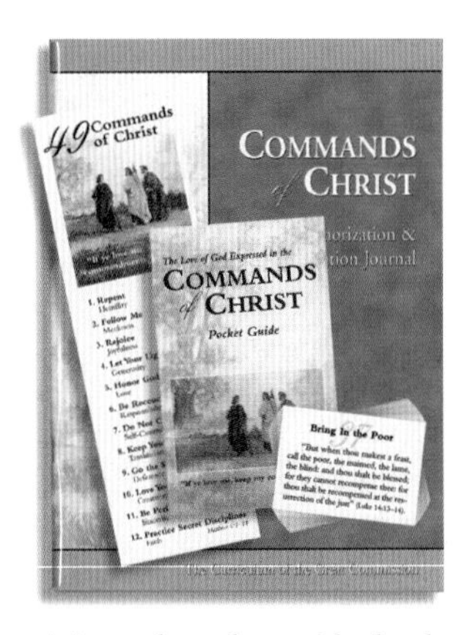

A journal, pocket guide, bookmark, and memorization cards for the commands are available.

The key to successful relationships is based on our ability to demonstrate specific character qualities. These qualities are the result of learning how to live out the commands of Christ, each of which results in a corresponding quality. For example, when we learn how to bring in the poor, we automatically develop the character quality of hospitality.

This rich, insightful series of studies explores forty-nine ways to love God and others. It explains each command and shows how to relate it to daily situations in life.

Each study guide contains more than ninety pages of valuable training with beautiful, full-color illustrations.

5. Receive Daily Success Commentaries.

Daily Success is a free, daily e-mail series that takes a detailed look at each of the forty-nine commands of Christ. Bill Gothard shares his insights on how these can be practically applied in everyday life. This forty-nine-week program includes seven e-mails for each command. To begin your free subscription and receive a supplemental book, visit www.dailysuccess.org today!

6. Teach Character From the World of Nature.

One of the most effective ways to learn character is to see how it is illustrated in the world of nature. Among our most loved publications, *Character Sketches* portray natural beauty and Biblical truths in stunning, lifelike watercolor. Each volume explores seven character qualities and examines four wildlife creatures and four people from the Bible who demonstrate each quality. You will be educated, encouraged, and dazzled by the nature lessons, powerful analogies, and amazing artistic detail that fill each of these books.

7. Remove the Stress of Financial Bondage.

In the Financial Freedom Seminar, Jim Sammons shares what he has discovered to be the principles needed to achieve financial freedom. Based on his own life story, he teaches how to get out of debt (and stay there), make wise investments, build the spirit of a marriage, and teach principles to children. His amazing story, wise insights, and winsome personality have been an inspiration to multitudes who have taken this seminar. *Men's Manual,* Volume 2 is a companion resource to this seminar.

Further information and pricing is available online at www.store.iblp.org or by calling 630-323-9610 or 800-398-1290.

Documentation

1. What Is Total Health?

1. Zodhiates, Spiros, ed. *The Hebrew-Greek Key Study Bible.* Chattanooga: AMG Publishers, 1991. 1680. To sanctify is to hallow and set apart for God. The Greek word is *hagiazō.* It stands in contrast to *koinos,* which means "defiled."
2. I Thessalonians 5:23–24
3. Genesis 1:26a
4. John 4:24
5. I Corinthians 2:14
6. See Romans 7:22–8:1.
7. Romans 8:6
8. Genesis 3:4
9. Zodhiates, 1711.
10. Matthew 11:29b
11. See John 14:21.
12. See Romans 5:12.
13. John 3:5, 7
14. John 3:4
15. II Corinthians 4:16b
16. See Ephesians 2:10.
17. Jeremiah 1:5. Another example of God designing the great work of a man before his birth was King Cyrus, who was prophesied by Jeremiah to rebuild the Temple. (See II Chronicles 36:22–23.)
18. Matthew 28:19–20a. The account of this commission in Mark 16:15–18 includes the sign of laying on of hands and healing, which is significant.
19. Deuteronomy 6:4, 7:15a
20. See Luke 17:11–19.
21. Leviticus 17:11a
22. Zodhiates, 1725.
23. Zodhiates, 1723.
24. NASA. "The Majestic Sombrero Galaxy (M104)." Photograph. *Heritage Project Celebrates Five Years of Harvesting the Best Images from Hubble Space Telescope Page.* HubbleSite. 29 Apr. 2008 <http://hubblesite.org/newscenter/archive/releases/2003/28/image/a>.
25. James 1:21b. The psalmist further emphasizes the importance of this aspect of salvation when he writes, "Thy word have I hid in mine heart, that I might not sin against thee" (Psalm 119:11).
26. III John 2
27. Galatians 6:8a
28. I Corinthians 5:5
29. Pottenger, Francis M., Jr., M.D. *Pottenger's Cats—A Study in Nutrition.* Lemon Grove, CA: Price-Pottenger Nutrition Foundation, 1995.

2. Is Total Health Total Healing?

1. Philippians 1:23
2. Psalm 71:17–18
3. Psalm 90:12
4. John 11:25
5. Galatians 6:8a
6. Deuteronomy 5:16a
7. Proverbs 30:17
8. See I Peter 1:15–16. Here Peter quotes from Leviticus 11:44, 19:2, 20:7.
9. I Corinthians 11:30
10. John 9:2–3
11. II Corinthians 12:9
12. Deuteronomy 28:27, 60–61
13. I Peter 5:8–9a

3. What Five Factors Determine Total Health?

1. Disease can be defined as an altered state of bodily function. These five root causes are categories that can include many related factors that will be explained.
2. Boeree, C. George, Ph.D. "General Psychology." Unpublished Article. 2002. 19–22. 21 Apr. 2008 <http://www.social-psychology.de/do/genpsy1.pdf>.
3. Guyton, Arthur C. and John E. Hall. *Textbook of Medical Physiology.* 11th ed. Philadelphia: W. B. Saunders Co., 2005. 205–07.
4. Guyton, 775–76.
5. Gershon, Michael D., M.D. *The Second Brain.* New York: HarperCollins, 2000.
6. Blakeslee, Sandra. "Complex and Hidden Brain in Gut Makes Stomachaches and Butterflies." *New York Times* 23 Jan. 1996. 26 Apr. 2008 http://query.nytimes.com/gst/fullpage.html?sec=health&res=980CE0DF1F39F930A15752C0A960958260.
7. Proverbs 23:7a
8. Proverbs 18:21a. See also James 3:5–8.
9. See Hebrews 4:12.
10. Proverbs 4:21–23
11. See Proverbs 25:18, James 3:5–8, Romans 3:13 and Psalm 64:3.
12. Roman 12:14
13. Hebrews 4:12
14. Psalm 16:7b
15. Proverbs 18:21
16. Galatians 6:7–8
17. Matthew 4:4
18. Romans 5:12
19. See Isaiah 58:8.

4. Does the Heart Think?

1. See Matthew 15:19.
2. See Proverbs 15:13.
3. See Daniel 1:8.
4. Pearsall, Paul, Ph.D., Gary E. R. Schwartz, Ph.D., and Linda G. S. Russek, Ph.D. "Changes in Heart Transplant Recipients That Parallel the Personalities of Their Donors." *Journal of Near-Death Studies* 20 No. 3 (2002): 191–206.
5. Jernigan, David A., Ph.D. *Everyday Miracles by God's Design.* Longwood, FL: Xulon Press, 2005. 40–41.
6. Gershon, Michael D., M.D. *The Second Brain.* New York: HarperCollins, 2000. 16.
7. Proverbs 4:23
8. "Amazing Heart Facts." *Nova Online.* PBS. 15 Feb. 2008 http://www.pbs.org/wgbh/nova/eheart/facts.html>.
9. Armour, J. Andrew. *Reflex Control of the Circulation.* Eds. Irving H. Zucker and Joseph P. Gilmore. Boca Raton: CRC Press, 1991. 1–37.
10. Armour, J. Andrew *Neurocardiology: Anatomical and Functional Principles.* New York: Oxford UP, 1994. 3–19.
11. Armour, J. Andrew "Cardiac Neuronal Hierarchy in Health and Disease." *American Journal of Physiology-Regul, Integr, and Comp Physiol* 287 (2004): 262-71.
12. "Head-Heart Interactions." *Science of the Heart Page.* Institute of HeartMath. 21 Apr. 2008 <http://www.heartmath.org/research/science-of-the-heart/soh_20.html>.
13. Matthew 12:34b
14. Matthew 15:18–19
15. Jernigan, 48.
16. Oschman, James L. *Energy Medicine and Human Performance.* Edinburgh: Butterworth Heinemann, 2003.
17. Lacey, Beatrice C. and John I. Lacey. "Two-Way Communication Between the Heart and the Brain." *American Psychologist* 33 (1978): 99–113.
18. McCraty, Rollin, Ph.D. "Influence of Cardiac Afferent Input on Heart-Brain Synchronization and Cognitive Performance." *International Journal of Psychophysiology* 45 (2002): 72–73.
19. Cardiac Coherence Increases Heart-Brain Synchronization." *Science of the Heart Page.* Institute of HeartMath. 22 Apr. 2008 <http://www.heartmath.org/research/science-of-the-heart/soh_22.html>.
20. Jeremiah 29:13
21. Psalm 119:10
22. II Corinthians 10:4–5
23. See Proverbs 23:7.
24. See Ephesians 5:19.
25. See I Samuel 16:14–23.

5. Factor 1: What We Think

1. Scripture associates the belief system with the heart. See Romans 10:9 and Acts 8:37.
2. James 3:8
3. Matthew 12:34b
4. The psalmist writes, "Thy word have I hid in mine heart, that I might not sin against thee" (Psalm 119:11). Notice he did not say, "Thy Word have I *memorized in my mind* that I might not sin against Thee."
5. Romans 7:15, 24
6. Strawbridge, W. J. et al. "Frequent Attendance at Religious Services and Mortality Over 28 Years." *American Journal of Public Health* 87 (1997): 957-61. Abstract. 18 Apr. 2008 <http://www.pubmedcentral.nih.gov/articlerender.fcgi?artid=1380930.>
7. Schwartz, Todd. "Psychologist and Scientist Suzanne Segerstrom '90 Studies Optimism and the Immune System." *L&C Chronicle* Summer 2003. 18 Apr. 2008. <http://www.lclark.edu/dept/chron/positives03.html>.
8. Proverbs 17:22
9. Grubert, John Peter. "Gravitational Frequencies of Extra-Solar Planets." *Lunar and Planetary Science* XXXV (2004).
10. *Home Page.* Dial-the-Truth Ministries. 18 Apr. 2008 <http://www.av1611.org/rockdead.html>.
11. Metropolitan Life Ins. Co., *Statistical Bulletin.* New York: Metro Life Ins. Co., 1980. 15.
12. Nordenberg, Tamar. "The Healing Power of Placebos." *FDA Consumer Magazine* 13 Dec. 1999. 20 Feb. 2008 <http://www.fda.gov/fdac/features/2000/100_heal.html>.
13. Carey, Benedict. "Antidepressant Studies Unpublished." *New York Times* 17 Jan. 2008. 21 Feb. 2008 <http://www.nytimes.com/2008/01/17/health/17depress.html>.

14. Kirsch, Irving et al. “Initial Severity and Antidepressant Benefits: A Meta-Analysis of Data Submitted to the Food and Drug Administration.” *PloS Medicine* 5 No. 2 (2008): e45. 18 Apr. 2008 <http://www.pubmedcentral.nih.gov/articlerender.fcgi?artid=2253608>.
15. Mark 11:23
16. Matthew 5:28
17. Proverbs 5:20–23
18. See Matthew 5:29–30.
19. Matthew 15:19–20a
20. The Biblical connections between stresses and bodily systems are explained later in this book.
21. See Matthew 17:20 and Zechariah 14:4.

6. Factor 2: What We Say

1. See James 3:5–8, Psalm 64:3, and Proverbs 25:18.
2. Proverbs 18:8
3. Proverbs 15:30b
4. Numbers 6:27
5. Luke 16:24
6. See I Timothy 4:4–5.
7. Proverbs 18:21
8. Matthew 12:36
9. Hebrews 4:12a
10. James 3:8
11. James 3:6
12. Guderian, Ronald, Ph.D. “Electric Shock for Human Snake Bites.” 6 July 2007. 21 Feb. 2008 <http://venomshock.wikidot.com/snake-bites-on-humans>.
13. Romans 12:14
14. I Peter 3:9
15. II Corinthians 10:5
16. Psalm 15:1–2
17. See Joshua 1:8 and Psalm 1:2.
18. I Thessalonians 5:17
19. John 10:10b
20. Proverbs 3:8
21. John 4:23
22. See Joshua 1:8.
23. See Matthew 4:4–10.
24. Proverbs 16:24
25. Genesis 4:10b
26. Psalm 51:1b–2
27. Genesis 1:2b
28. See John 3:8.
29. See Acts 2:2.
30. Proverbs 18:21a
31. Mark 11:22–23
32. Romans 10:8b–10, 13
33. I Peter 3:9

7. Factor 3: What We Do

1. See Romans 2:15.
2. See Genesis 3:7–8.
3. I John 1:9
4. Proverbs 28:13
5. Romans 3:23
6. Romans 6:23
7. Romans 4:15b
8. Hebrews 2:2–3a
9. Genesis 2:23
10. Psalm 6:2
11. Psalm 6:3a
12. Psalm 32:1, 3
13. Proverbs 3:7
14. See II Thessalonians 2:10–12.
15. Schizophrenia is a problem in the soul, not the body. It is the result of a conflicting mind, will, and emotions. The description of James identifies the problem: “A double minded man is unstable in all his ways” (James 1:8). Researchers have not yet found a direct physiological cause of schizophrenia.
16. See II Thessalonians 2:11.
17. See Proverbs 28:13.
18. “Irish Scientist Discovers New Strain of AIDS Virus.” *CDC HIV/Hepatitis STD/TB Prevention News Update* 9 July 2003. 20 Feb. 2008 <http://www.thebodypro.com/content/art28615.html>.
19. Henkel, John. “Hepatitis C: New Treatment Helps Some, But Cure Remains Elusive.” *FDA Consumer Magazine* 10 Feb. 1999. 20 Feb. 2008 <http://www.fda.gov/fdac/features/1999/299_hepc.html>.
20. Kitagawa, Masanobu et al. “Friend Leukemia Virus Infection Enhances DNA Damage-Induced Apoptosis of Hematopoietic Cells, Causing Lethal Anemia in C3H Hosts.” *Journal of Virology* 76 No. 15 (2002): 7790–98.
21. Marco, Michael. “Acquired Immunodeficiency Syndrome-Related Cancers: the Community Perspective.” *Journal of the National Cancer Institute Monographs* 1998 No. 23 (1998): 21–22.
22. Lloyd, A. “HIV Infection and Aids.” *Papua New Guinea Medical Journal* 39 (1996): 174–80.
23. *The Immune System and Radiation Page.* Hanford Health Information Network. 21 Apr. 2008 <http://www.doh.wa.gov/hanford/publications/overview/immune.html>.
24. Wicks, Robert. “Friedrich Nietzsche.” *Stanford Encyclopedia of Philosophy* Spring 2008 ed., Ed. Edward N. Zalta. 21 Apr. 2008 <http://plato.stanford.edu/archives/spr2008/entries/nietzsche/>.

8. Factor 4: What We Eat

1. Luke 4:4
2. Luke 5:5
3. Ephesians 6:3
4. Proverbs 15:17
5. Matthew 15:17–19
6. McDaniel, T. C., Ph.D. *Disease Reprieve.* Philadelphia: Xlibris Corp., 1999.
7. Witkowski, J. A. “Dr. Carrel’s Immortal Cells.” *Medical History* 24 (1980): 129–42.
8. *Are Cells Immortal? Page.* Zunami Healthy Hydration. 20 Feb. 2008 <http://www.zunami.com/Are-Cells-Immortal.php>.
9. See Leviticus 17:11.
10. Purich, Daniel L. and R. Donald Allison. *Handbook of Biochemical Kinetics.* Durham: Academic Press, 1999.
11. Riddick, Thomas M. *Control of Colloidal Stability Through Zeta Potential.* Wynnewood: Livingston Publishing Co., 1968.
12. McDaniel.
13. Hunter, Robert J. *Foundations of Colloid Science* 2nd ed. New York: Oxford UP, 2001.
14. Chenoweth, Bruce. *Alkaline Ash / Acid Ash Foods Page.* ABCompany. 16 Apr. 2008 <http://www.docgolob.com/abco/aw/nutrition/alkaacid.htm.>
15. The medical term for sticky blood is *agglutination,* which can be seen in the coagulation of blood when it is exposed to trauma or oxygen.
16. Brewer, A. Keith, Ph.D. “The High pH Therapy for Cancer Tests on Mice and Humans.” *Pharmacology Biochemistry and Behavior* 21 (1984): 1–5.
17. Caracalla, V. T. “Basic Methods of Quality Control: pH Measurements.” *Manual on Simple Methods of Meat Preservation.* N.p.: FAO of the UN Rome, 1990.
18. Sellmeyer, Deborah E., Katie L. Stone, and Anthony Sebastian. “A High Ratio of Dietary Animal to Vegetable Protein Increases the Rate of Bone Loss and the Risk of Fracture in Postmenopausal Women.” *American Journal of Clinical Nutrition* 73 No. 1 (2001): 118–22.
19. Bushinsky, David A. et al. “Chronic Acidosis-Induced Alteration in Bone Bicarbonate Phosphate.” *American Journal of Physiology-Renal Physiology* 285 (2003): 532–39.
20. See Leviticus 11 and Acts 15:29.
21. Deuteronomy 7:15a
22. Sohal, Rajindar S. and Richard Weindruch. “Oxidative Stress, Caloric Restriction, and Aging.” *Science* 5 July 1996: 59–63.
23. Yu, B. P. and H. Y. Chung. “Stress Resistance by Caloric Restriction for Longevity.” *Annals of the New York Academy of Sciences* 928 (2001): 39–47.
24. Goodrick, Charles L. et al. “Effects of Intermittent Feeding Upon Growth, Activity, and Lifespan in Rats Allowed Voluntary Exercise.” *Experimental Aging Research* 9 No. 3 (1983): 203–09.
25. See Luke 18:11–12.
26. Matthew 6:17–18
27. “What Are the Symptoms of Dehydration?” *FAQ Page.* Rehydration Project. 16 Apr. 2008 <http://rehydrate.org/faq/what_are_the_symptoms_of_dehydration.htm>.
28. This is consistent with current medical recommendations.

    Mayo Clinic Staff. “Water: How Much Should You Drink Every Day?” *Food and Nutrition Page.* Mayo Clinic. 19 Apr. 2008 <http://www.mayoclinic.com/health/water/NU00283>.
29. Batmanghelidj, F., M.D. *Your Body’s Many Cries for Water.* Vienna, VA: Global Health Solutions Inc., 1997.
30. See Psalm 104:14.
31. See I Timothy 5:23.
32. Grapes contain iron, potassium, and fiber. They are powerful detoxifiers and can improve the condition of the skin and treat gout, liver problems, and kidney disorders. Research has revealed that resveratrol, a natural substance produced by grapes, can help inhibit the formation of tumors and that purple grape juice may be even more effective than aspirin in reducing the risk of heart attack.
33. Chou, E. J. et al. “Effect of Ingestion of Purple Grape Juice on Endothelial Function in Patients With Heart Disease.” *American Journal of Cardiology* 88 No. 5 (2001): 553–55.
34. Anselm, Eric et al. “Grape Juice Causes Endothelium-Dependent Relaxation via a Redox-Sensitive Src- and Akt-Dependent Activation of eNOS.” *Cardiovascular Research* 73 No. 2 (2007): 404–13.

35. Singletary, Keith W. et al. "Anthocyanin-Rich Grape Extract Blocks Breast Cell DNA Damage." *Journal of Medicinal Food* 10 No. 2 (2007): 244–51.
36. See Isaiah 38:21.
37. The solution to impotence in the days of Abraham was a type of mandrake with possible aphrodisiac properties. See Genesis 30:14–27.
38. See I Kings 19:5–8.
39. Psalm 104:14

9. Factor 5: What We Inherit

1. See I Corinthians 15:21–22. Since you are in Adam, you are a part of everything that Adam did. When you were born again, you retroactively became a part of everything that Jesus did, including His perfect life and death.
2. Romans 5:12
3. See Hebrews 7:9–10.
4. *Genetic Disorders Page.* Medline Plus. 25 Jan. 2008 <http://www.nlm.nih.gov/medlineplus/geneticdisorders.html>.
5. Elbein, Steven C. "The Genetics of Human Non-insulin-Dependent (Type 2) Diabetes Mellitus." *Journal of Nutrition* 127 No. 9 (1997): 1891–96.
6. I Corinthians 15:22
7. This includes dishonor toward parents, See Exodus 20:12 and Ephesians 6:3.
8. Psalm 90:8–10. This Psalm was written by Moses, who lived 120 years (forty years in Egypt, forty years in exile, and forty years leading the people through the wilderness). In this Psalm, he explains to the people of Israel that their shortened life span was a consequence of their disobedience of God's commands.
9. Desiere, Frank. "Towards a Systems Biology Understanding of Human Health: Interplay Between Genotype, Environment, and Nutrition." *Biotechnology Annual Review* 10 (2004): 51–84.
10. Emmons, Robert A. and Michael E. McCullough. "Counting Blessings Versus Burdens: An Experimental Investigation of Gratitude and Subjective Well-Being in Daily Life." *Journal of Personality and Social Psychology* 84 No. 2 (2003): 377–89.
11. See John 9.
12. See Acts 3:2–8.
13. See Genesis 16:1, 17:15–16, 18:11.
14. Jeremiah 33:3
15. Gothard, Bill. *The Power of Crying Out.* Sisters, OR: Multnomah Publishers, 2002.

10. How Does Stress Cause Disease?

1. Cohen, S., D. A. Tyrrell, and A. P. Smith. "Psychological Stress and Susceptibility to the Common Cold." *New England Journal of Medicine* 325 No. 9 (1991): 606–12.
2. Schleifer, S. J. et al. "Suppression of Lymphocyte Stimulation Following Bereavement." *Journal of the American Medical Association* 250 (1993): 374–77.
3. Gorard, D. A. "Escalating Polypharmacy." *QJM: An International Journal of Medicine* 99 No. 11 (2006): 797–800.
4. Einarson, T. R. "Drug-Related Hospital Admissions." *Annals of Pharmacotherapy* 27 No. 7 (1993): 832–40.
5. Thomson Healthcare Staff. *Physician's Desk Reference.* 62nd ed. Montvale, NJ: Thomson Healthcare, 2007. 1837–38.
6. Kennedy, Barbara Ferguson. "Milk and Dairy Products—You're Better Off Without Them." *Healthy Eating Page.* National Health Association. 4 Apr. 2008 <http://www.healthscience.org/content/view/353/123/>.
7. Hamer, Ryke Greed. *The New German Medicine.* 28 Jan. 2008 <http://www.newmedicine.ca/index.php>.
   We are grateful to Dr. Hamer for such a powerful affirmation of the relationship between stress and disease. This association is confirmed by many doctors, such as Dr. Billy Boring, M.D., from McKinney, TX, who stated, "At least 70% of my patients have sicknesses and diseases that are directly related to stress."
8. The seven stresses are illustrated in the following passages of Matthew 5, 6, and 7:
   Anger—Matthew 5:21–22
   Guilt—Matthew 5:23–24
   Lust—Matthew 5:27–32
   Bitterness—Matthew 5:38–48
   Greed—Matthew 6:19–30
   Fear—Matthew 6:31–34
   Envy—Matthew 7:7–12
9. Matthew 7:28b–29a
10. Researchers classify bodily systems differently. We have chosen seven primary ones, which several others can be grouped with.
11. See Proverbs 14:30.
12. Material taken from the notes of: Billica, Roger, Ph.D. "Achieving Health Without Treating Diseases." Lecture. Total Health Seminar. IBLP. ITC, Indianapolis. 3 Oct. 2007.
13. Guyton, Arthur C. and John E. Hall. *Textbook of Medical Physiology.* 11th ed. Philadelphia: W. B. Saunders Co., 2005. 731–34.
14. Ruggerio, David A. Ph.D. "Thalamocortical, Reticular, and Limbic Systems." Lecture. Columbia University College, New York. 4 Feb. 2006. Transcript. 21 Apr. 2008 <http://neuroscienceupdate.cumc.columbia.edu/popups/transcript_ruggiero.html>.
15. Dhabhar, Firdaus S. "Acute Stress Enhances While Chronic Stress Suppresses Skin Immunity: The Role of Stress Hormones and Leukocyte Trafficking." *Annals of the New York Academy of Sciences* 917 (2000): 876–93.
16. See 12.
17. Psalm 139:14
18. Psalm 103:2–3
19. John 14:21
20. John 15:10a
21. I John 2:3, 5
22. I John 3:22a
23. John 14:23
24. John 15:14

11. How Does Anger Affect the Cardiovascular System?

1. *Cardiovascular Disease Statistics.* American Heart Association. 28 Jan. 2008 <http://www.americanheart.org/presenter.jhtml?identifier=4478>.
2. Ibid.
3. Folkman, Judah, M.D. "The Discovery of Angiogenesis Inhibitors: A New Class of Drugs." Lecture. Marine Biological Laboratory, Woods Hole, MA. 15 June 2001. Transcript. 20 Apr. 2008 <http://www.mblwhoilibrary.org/services/lecture_series/folkman/>.
4. Bleil, Maria E. et al. "Anger-Related Personality Traits and Carotid Artery Atherosclerosis in Untreated Hypertensive Men." *Psychosomatic Medicine* 66 (2004): 633–39.
5. Williams, Janice E. et al. "Anger Proneness Predicts Coronary Heart Disease Risk." *Circulation* 101 No. 17 (2000): 2034–39.
6. See I Samuel 25:3.
7. See I Samuel 25:37.
8. *Autonomic Nervous System Disorders Page.* Medline Plus. 28 Jan. 2008 <http://www.nlm.nih.gov/medlineplus/autonomicnervoussystemdisorders.html>.
9. Proverbs 19:19
10. II Chronicles 16:10
11. See II Chronicles 16:12.
12. Guyton, Arthur C. and John E. Hall. *Textbook of Medical Physiology.* 11th ed. Philadelphia: W. B. Saunders Co., 2005. 848–50.
13. Gordon, D. J. and B. M. Rifkind. "High-Density Lipoprotein: the Clinical Implications of Recent Studies." *New England Journal of Medicine* 321 No. 19 (1989): 1311–16.
14. Steprans, Ilona et al. "Oxidized Cholesterol in the Diet Accelerates the Development of Aortic Atherosclerosis in Cholesterol-Fed Rabbits." *Arteriosclerosis, Thrombosis, and Vascular Biology* 18 No. 6 (1998): 977–83.
15. Guyton, 952.
16. Mittleman, Murray A. et al. "Triggering of Acute Myocardial Infarction Onset by Episodes of Anger." *Circulation* 92 No. 7 (1995): 1720–25.
17. Burr, Harold Saxton, Ph.D. *Blueprint for Immortality: The Electric Patterns of Life.* Essex: C. W. Daniel Co. Ltd., 1972.
18. James 1:6, 8
19. Proverbs 27:4a
20. Romans 2:5
21. Matthew 4:17
22. Proverbs 13:10
23. James 4:6b
24. Psalm 62:5
25. Psalm 51:4a
26. Hebrews 12:17b
27. See Psalm 51.
28. Matthew 25:40b
29. Acts 9:5b
30. Matthew 5:11–12a
31. I Thessalonians 5:16, 18
32. Romans 8:28
33. Romans 5:3b–4
34. II Timothy 2:12a
35. Lamentations 3:27, 30
36. Matthew 5:12b
37. Matthew 18:15a
38. Proverbs 18:17
39. Psalm 15:3, 5
40. Proverbs 26:20
41. Matthew 5:44b
42. Matthew 6:21
43. Proverbs 18:21a
44. James 5:16
45. Matthew 5:48

46. Matthew 5:46–48
47. Matthew 5:45
48. Matthew 15:14a
49. Proverbs 18:21
50. Proverbs 30:17
51. Matthew 5:41
52. Matthew 6:21

12. How Does Guilt Affect the Nervous System?

1. Examples of impaired communication with God include Matthew 5:23–24 and Psalm 66:18. The importance of keeping a good conscience with others is emphasized in I Timothy 1:19–20.
2. Andreassi, John L. *Psychophysiology: Human Behavior and Physiological Response.* New York: Routledge, 2006. 50.
3. Jones, David S., M.D. and Sheila Quinn. *Textbook of Functional Medicine.* Gig Harbor, WA: Institute for Functional Medicine, 2005. 259.
4. Romans 2:15
5. Romans 3:23
6. See I Timothy 1:19.
7. Romans 4:15b
8. Matthew 7:22–23
9. Isaiah 53:6
10. See Genesis 3:7.
11. Proverbs 28:13
12. See Genesis 3:8.
13. Romans 1:23a
14. See Genesis 3:12–13.
15. I Samuel 15:19–20a
16. I Samuel 15:13b, 15
17. See Numbers 5:27–28.
18. II Kings 5:25
19. Genesis 4:9
20. Romans 2:1
21. See II Chronicles 16:10.
22. See Exodus 22:1.
23. See II Samuel 12:7.
24. See I Samuel 2:22, 25; 3:12–14.
25. See II Samuel 13:22–29.
26. See Proverbs 1:11–19.
27. See Jonah 4:8 and I Kings 19:2–4.
28. "What Causes Depression?" *Depression Page.* NIMH. 20 Apr. 2008 <http://www.nimh.nih.gov/health/publications/depression/causes-of-depression.shtml>.
29. *The Numbers Count: Mental Disorders in America Page.* NIMH. 20 Apr. 2008 <http://www.nimh.nih.gov/health/publications/the-numbers-count-mental-disorders-in-america.shtml>.
30. "Depression." *Disorders Management Page.* WHO. 23 Apr. 2008 <http://www.who.int/mental_health/management/depression/definition/en/>.
31. Looper, Karl J. "Potential Medical and Surgical Complications of Serotonergic Antidepressant Medications." *Psychosomatics* 48 No. 1 (2007): 1–9.
32. Fava, Giovanni A. "Can Long-Term Treatment With Antidepressant Drugs Worsen the Course of Depression?" *Journal of Clinical Psychiatry* 64 No. 2 (2003): 123–33.
33. "FDA Proposes New Warnings About Suicidal Thinking, Behavior in Young Adults Who Take Antidepressant Medications." *FDA News Page.* U.S. FDA. 20 Apr. 2008 <http://www.fda.gov/bbs/topics/NEWS/2007/NEW01624.html>.
34. Boyles, Salynn. "Are Antidepressants Effective?" *Medical News Page.* WebMD. 20 Apr. 2008 <http://www.webmd.com/depression/news/20020710/are-antidepressants-effective>.
35. Psalm 51:10
36. Elias, Marilyn. "Prozac Linked to Child Suicide Risk; Study Finds 50% Greater Chance; Companies Defend Antidepressants." *USA Today* 14 Sep. 2004, final ed.: A01. 17 Apr. 2008 <http://www.usatoday.com/news/health/2004-09-13-prozac_x.htm>.
37. "Veteran Suicides." *CBS Evening News with Katie Couric.* CBS. WCBS, New York. 4 Dec. 2007. Transcript. 17 Apr. 2008 <http://www.cbsnews.com/stories/2007/11/13/cbsnews_investigates/main3498625.shtml>.
38. Proverbs 24:11–12
39. See 37.
40. Psalm 32:3–4
41. John 3:7
42. I Corinthians 15:22a
43. Romans 10:10–11
44. See Numbers 21:6–9.
45. See John 3:14–15.
46. See Psalm 1:3.
47. Matthew 22:37
48. Matthew 15:8
49. James 4:4–5
50. See John 21:15–17.
51. See Romans 5:8.
52. Matthew 11:15
53. II Timothy 3:16a
54. Luke 4:4
55. Ephesians 6:17
56. John 15:7
57. Matthew 18:16b
58. See Proverbs 1:8.
59. See I Timothy 5:17.
60. See Philippians 1:12.
61. See Acts 2:17.
62. See Psalm 66:18.
63. See Isaiah 50:4.
64. Matthew 26:26b–27
65. I Corinthians 11:28
66. There is clear Scriptural evidence that the Lord's Supper and communion are two separate events. They may be celebrated together, as Jesus did with His disciples (see Matthew 26:26–28), or they may be carried out separately, as Paul directed the Corinthian church to do (see I Corinthians 11:20).

    The Lord's Supper involves an actual meal. It was celebrated as the Passover feast. On the other hand, communion took place after the meal and consists of the bread and the cup.

    The Passover feast was carried out just before the nation of Israel left Egypt for the Promised Land. Types of the bread and the cup took place later in the wilderness. (See John 6:32–36, 48–51 and I Corinthians 10:1–4.)
67. The Lord's Table is based on the Passover feast. Every father conducted this feast in his own home. He had the responsibility of providing a lamb and putting its blood on the doorposts and the lintel. Then on the Passover night, he gathered his family around the slain lamb and under its blood.

    Whereas many other Jewish holidays revolved around the synagogue, the Passover dinner (seder) continued to be celebrated in the homes. The meal is family-based because its purpose is for a father to teach his family, especially his sons, the importance of the occasion. (See Exodus 13:8.)
68. See Luke 22:10–12.
69. See Luke 24:30–35.
70. See Acts 2:41–46.
71. I Corinthians 11:20, 22
72. See Ephesians 4:26–27.
73. Revelation 3:20a
74. Matthew 18:20
75. Matthew 5:23–24a
76. See Matthew 5:23.
77. James 4:9–10
78. See Acts 24:16.
79. Matthew 7:1
80. Romans 2:1
81. James 4:11–12
82. Matthew 22:37–40
83. Zodhiates, Spiros, ed. *The Hebrew-Greek Key Study Bible.* Chattanooga: AMG Publishers, 1991. 1731.
84. Zodhiates, 1704.
85. See II Samuel 19:35.
86. II Timothy 4:2b
87. See II Samuel 12:1–7.
88. Matthew 5:37
89. Matthew 12:37
90. Proverbs 6:1–2
91. Ecclesiastes 5:4, 6
92. Psalm 15:4b

13. How Does Lust Affect the Endocrine System?

1. "Hormone." *Online Etymology Dictionary.* 2001. 19 Feb. 2008 <http://www.etymonline.com/index.php?search=hormone&searchmode=none>.
2. Guyton, Arthur C. and John E. Hall. *Textbook of Medical Physiology.* 11th ed. Philadelphia: W. B. Saunders Co., 2005. 963.
3. Ruggerio, David A. Ph.D. "Thalamocortical, Reticular, and Limbic Systems." Lecture. Columbia University College, New York. 4 Feb. 2006. Transcript. 21 Apr. 2008 <http://neuroscienceupdate.cumc.columbia.edu/popups/transcript_ruggiero.html>.
4. Alexander, Linda L., Ph.D. et al. "Sexually Transmitted Diseases in America: How Many Cases and at What Cost?" *American Social Health Reports Page.* ASHA. <http://www.ashastd.org/pdfs/std_rep.pdf>.
5. Weinstock, Hillard, Stuart Berman, and Willard Cates, Jr. "Sexually Transmitted Diseases Among American Youth: Incidence and Prevalence Estimates, 2000." *Perspectives on Sexual and Reproductive Health* 36 No. 1 (2004): 6–10.
6. Galatians 6:8a
7. Alan Guttmacher Institute. *Sex and America's Teenagers.* New York: Alan Guttmacher Institute, 1994.
8. NIH. "Your Kidneys and How They Work." *Kidney and Urologic Diseases Page.* NKUDIC. 22 Apr. 2008 <http://kidney.niddk.nih.gov/kudiseases/pubs/yourkidneys/index.htm#rate>.

9. "FDA Announces Revisions to Labels for Cialis, Levitra and Viagra." *FDA News Page.* USFDA. 22 Apr. 2008 <http://www.fda.gov/bbs/topics/NEWS/2007/NEW01730.html>.
10. Guyton, 1020.
11. Guyton, 735.
12. Zodhiates, Spiros, ed. *The Hebrew-Greek Key Study Bible.* Chattanooga: AMG Publishers, 1991. 1613.
13. See Genesis 3:6.
14. See Exodus 20:17.
15. See Matthew 5:27–30.
16. Romans 7:5, 18a
17. Romans 6:12–14
18. Andrews, R. C. et al. "Abnormal Cortisol Metabolism and Tissue Sensitivity to Cortisol in Patients with Glucose Intolerance." *Journal of Clinical Endocrinology & Metabolism* 87 No. 12 (2002): 5587–93.
19. Genesis 3:6
20. Romans 5:12
21. Epel, Elissa S. et al. "Stress and Body Shape: Stress-Induced Cortisol Secretion is Consistently Greater Among Women With Central Fat." *Psychosomatic Medicine* 62 No. 5 (2000): 623–32.
22. Eberhart, M. S., Ph.D. et al. "Prevalence of Overweight and Obesity Among Adults With Diagnosed Diabetes—United States, 1988–1994 and 1999-2002." *Morbidity and Mortality Weekly Report* 53 No. 45 (2004): 1066–68.
23. Zimmet, Paul, K. G. M. M. Alberti, and Jonathan Shaw. "Global and Societal Implications of the Diabetes Epidemic." *Nature* 414 No. 6865 (2001): 782–87.
24. "Prevalence of Overweight and Obesity Among Adults: United States, 1999-2002." *Health eStats Page.* NCHS. 19 Feb. 2008 <http://www.cdc.gov/nchs/products/pubs/pubd/hestats/obese/obse99.htm>.
25. Xu, Haiyan et al. "Chronic Inflammation in Fat Plays a Crucial Role in the Development of Obesity-Related Insulin Resistance." *Journal of Clinical Investigation* 112 No. 12 (2003): 1821–30.
26. Unger, Roger H. "Lipotoxic Diseases." *Annual Review of Medicine* 53 (2002): 319–36.
27. Proietto, J. and A. W. Thorburn. "The Therapeutic Potential of Leptin." *Expert Opinion on Investigational Drugs* 12 No. 3 (2003): 373–78.
28. Considine, Robert V. et al. "Serum Immunoreactive-Leptin Concentrations in Normal-Weight and Obese Humans." *New England Journal of Medicine* 334 No. 5 (1996): 292–95.
29. See Genesis 2:16–17, 3:6.
30. See Genesis 4:5, 8.
31. See Mark 6:21-26.
32. See Matthew 24:38–39 and Genesis 6:1–5.
33. Ephesians 2:3
34. I Peter 2:11
35. James 1:14–15
36. See Mark 8:33.
37. II Corinthians 10:4–5
38. See Genesis 6:5.
39. Matthew 24:37
40. Proverbs 23:7a
41. Matthew 15:19–20a
42. See Genesis 6:5.
43. Proverbs 4:23
44. See I Corinthians 6:13.
45. See Romans 12:1–2.
46. See Romans 6:19.
47. I Corinthians 9:27. See also I Corinthians 9:24 and Hebrews 12:1–3.
48. Galatians 6:8
49. Proverbs 7:22–23a. From a hunter's perspective, this means that the victim will die a slow death. A dart through the heart or lungs will bring about swift destruction, but prey with a pierced liver will run off, unaware that it is in the process of dying. The dart will cause internal bleeding with little pain.
50. Hoofnagle, Jay H. "Hepatitis." *The World Book Encyclopedia* Vol. 9. 2003 ed. 2003.
51. Orduna A. et al. "Infection by Hepatitis B and C Virus in Non-Intravenous Drug Using Female Prostitutes in Spain." *European Journal of Epidemiology* 8 No. 5 (1992): 656–59.
52. See Proverbs 23:29–33.
53. Worman, Howard J., M.D. "Alcoholic Liver Disease." *Diseases of the Liver Page.* CUMC. 23 Apr. 2008 <http://www.cumc.columbia.edu/dept/gi/alcohol.html>.
54. Selye, Hans. *The Stress of Life.* London: Longmans, Green & Co., 1957. 205.
55. de Bono, J. S. et al. "Metastatic Extragonadal Seminoma Associated With Cardiac Transplantation." *Annals of Oncology* 11 No. 6 (2000): 749–52.
56. Reichrath, Jorg. *Molecular Mechanisms of Basal Cell and Squamous Cell Carcinomas.* Georgetown, TX: Landes Bioscience, 2006.
57. Psalm 119:11
58. John 15:3, 7
59. John 17:17
60. Romans 8:6
61. Proverbs 16:25
62. See Romans 1:28.
63. See II Thessalonians 2:10–11.
64. Deuteronomy 29:18–19
65. Phillips, J. B. *The New Testament in Modern English.* New York: Macmillan, 1962.
66. See I Corinthians 5:1–8.
67. I Corinthians 5:5
68. II Timothy 2:22
69. Proverbs 7:22–23
70. Proverbs 23:31–33
71. David recognized that his sin of immorality was against God. See Psalm 51:4.
72. Psalm 50:15
73. Galatians 5:9
74. Psalm 119:11
75. Proverbs 4:23
76. See Matthew 4:1–11.
77. See Nehemiah 2–4.
78. "May 29, 1453—Byzantium: "The Last Day of the World." *Lives & Events Page.* Christian History Institute. 22 Apr. 2008 <http://chi.gospelcom.net/DAILYF/2001/05/daily-05-29-2001.shtml>.
79. Matthew 5:17
80. Romans 7:7b
81. Romans 3:19b
82. See Genesis 1:28–30.
83. See Exodus 20:3–19.
84. See Matthew 22:37–40.
85. See Mark 10:5.
86. Matthew 5:27
87. See Matthew 28:20.
88. John 1:17
89. I John 5:3b
90. Luke 24:32
91. Matthew 5:28
92. Matthew 15:19
93. Burr, Harold Saxton, Ph.D. *Blueprint for Immortality: The Electric Patterns of Life.* Essex: C. W. Daniel Co. Ltd., 1972.
94. See II Corinthians 2:16.
95. Matthew 5:8
96. John 7:38
97. Matthew 6:4b
98. Hebrews 11:6
99. Hebrews 11:24–26a
100. See James 5:16.
101. See Psalm 50:15.
102. See Daniel 1:8.
103. Matthew 7:14b
104. See Genesis 5:24.
105. Zodhiates, 1613.
106. I John 1:7
107. Proverbs 4:18
108. Genesis 39:9b
109. Matthew 7:15
110. II Peter 2:1–2, 14, 19
111. See Romans 5:17, 20; 6:1–2; 6:14; and Titus 2:11–12.
112. Gothard, Bill. *The Exceeding Great Power of God's Grace.* Oak Brook, IL: Institute in Basic Life Principles, 2006.
113. I Corinthians 15:10
114. Jude 4a
115. Luke 12:1b
116. I Corinthians 5:6b–7a
117. I Corinthians 5:2
118. I Corinthians 13:4
119. Matthew 16:12b
120. Matthew 15:6b–9
121. Matchak, Jacob. Telephone Interview. 29 Apr. 2008.
122. Matthew 15:6b
123. Matthew 19:6b
124. See Romans 6:13–16.
125. I Corinthians 7:4
126. See I Corinthians 7:5.
127. See Hebrews 13:4.
128. Genesis 29:20b
129. See I Corinthians 13:4–8.

14. How Does Bitterness Affect the Digestive System?

1. Insel, Paul, R. Elaine Turner, and Don Ross. *Nutrition.* 2nd ed. Kendallville, IN: Jones and Bartlett Publishers Inc., 2003. 114.
2. Krantz, Bryan A. et al. "A Phenylalanine Clamp Catalyzes Protein Translocation Through the Anthrax Toxin Pore." *Science* 309 No. 5735 (2005): 777–81.
3. Takahashi, I. et al. "Gut as the Largest Immunologic Tissue." *Journal of Parenteral and Enteral Nutrition* 23 No. 5 (1999): 7–12.
4. Brandtzaeg, P. "Development and Basic Mechanisms of Human Gut Immunity." *Nutrition Reviews* 56 No. 1 (1998): 5–18.
5. Kalach, N. et al. "Intestinal Permeability in Children: Variation With Age and Reliability in the

Diagnosis of Cow's Milk Allergy." *Acta Paediatrica* 90 No. 5 (2001): 499–504.

6. Rooney, P. J., R. T. Jenkins, and W. W. Buchanan. "A Short Review of the Relationship Between Intestinal Permeability and Inflammatory Joint Disease." *Clinical and Experimental Rheumatology* 8 No. 1 (1990): 75–83.
7. Darlington, L. G. and N. W. Ramsey. "Review of Dietary Therapy for Rheumatoid Arthritis." *British Journal of Rheumatology* 32 No. 6 (1993): 507–14.
8. Smith, M. D., R. A. Gibson, and P. M. Brooks. "Abnormal Bowel Permeability in Ankylosing Spondylitis and Rheumatoid Arthritis." *Journal of Rheumatology* 12 No. 2 (1985): 299–305.
9. Takahashi.
10. Gershon, Michael D., M.D. *The Second Brain.* New York: HarperCollins, 2000.
11. Ruggerio, David A. Ph.D. "Thalamo-cortical, Reticular, and Limbic Systems." Lecture. Columbia University College, New York. 4 Feb. 2006. Transcript. 21 Apr. 2008 <http://neuroscienceupdate.cumc.columbia.edu/popups/transcript_ruggiero.html>.
12. Guyton, Arthur C. and John E. Hall. *Textbook of Medical Physiology.* 11th ed. Philadelphia: W. B. Saunders Co., 2005. 820.
13. Guyton, 797–99.
14. Bosch, Jos A. et al. "Salivary MUC5B-Mediated Adherence (Ex Vivo) of Helicobacter Pylori During Acute Stress." *Psychosomatic Medicine* 62 No. 1 (2000): 40–49.
15. Guyton, 820–821.
16. Kiba, Takayoshi. "Relationships between the Autonomic Nervous System, Humoral Factors and Immune Functions in the Intestine." *Digestion* 74 No. 3–4 (2006): 215–27.
17. van Thiel, David H. et al. "Gastrointestinal Transit in Cirrhotic Patients: Effect of Hepatic Encephalopathy and its Treatment." *Hepatology* 19 No. 1 (1994): 67–71.
18. Khan, S. A. et al. "DNA Adducts, Detected by 32P Postlabelling, in Human Cholangiocarcinoma." *GUT* 52 No. 4 (2003): 586–91.
19. Chida, Y., N. Sudo, and C. Kubo. "Psychological Stress Impairs Hepatic Blood Flow via Central CRF Receptors in Mice." *Life Science* 76 No. 15 (2005): 1707–12.
20. Guyton, 803.
21. Everhart, James E., M.D., M.P.H. *Digestive Diseases in the United States: Epidemiology and Impact.* Washington D.C.: NIH, 1994.
22. See Matthew 9:22; Mark 5:34, 10:52; and Luke 8:48, 17:19.
23. See Matthew 17:20 and Luke 17:6.
24. Mark 11:24–26
25. "Where Doctors, Hospitals and Patients Fall Short." *Poor Performance Page.* Free-Market Medicine. 28 Apr. 2008 <http://www.marketmed.org/fallshort.asp?fmmfont=fontsml>.
26. Matthew 18:34–35
27. Douyon, Liselle and David E. Schteingart. "Effect of Obesity and Starvation on Thyroid Hormone, Growth Hormone, and Cortisol Secretion." *Endocrinology and Metabolism Clinics of North America* 31 No. 1 (2002): 173–89.
28. Jones, David S., M.D. and Sheila Quinn. *Textbook of Functional Medicine.* Gig Harbor, WA: Institute for Functional Medicine, 2005. 649–50.
29. Guyton, 952.
30. See II Samuel 6:20–23.
31. Feng Li, Xiao et al. "Stress-Induced Suppression of the Gonadotropin-Releasing Hormone Pulse Generator in the Female Rat: A Novel Neural Action for Calcitonin Gene-Related Peptide." *Endocrinology* 145 No. 4 (2004): 1556–63.
32. Guyton, 1020.
33. Jones, David S., M.D. and Sheila Quinn. *Textbook of Functional Medicine.* Gig Harbor, WA: Institute for Functional Medicine, 2005. 649–50.
34. Guyton, 952.
35. II Chronicles 21:15
36. II Chronicles 21:18–19a
37. Colossians 3:12
38. See Romans 8:28.
39. See I Thessalonians 5:18.
40. Proverbs 18:21a
41. See Jeremiah 33:8 and I John 1:9. For a testimony of the scars in Jesus' hands and side, see John 20:20, 25, 27.
42. See Genesis 42.
43. Matthew 24:42
44. Hebrews 10:34–35
45. Matthew 5:11–12a
46. I John 3:2b–3
47. I Thessalonians 4:16a
48. I Thessalonians 4:16b–17
49. II Corinthians 5:10
50. Revelation 21:4a
51. Luke 9:23
52. II Corinthians 4:10–12
53. Luke 9:24
54. Zodhiates, Spiros, ed. *The Hebrew-Greek Key Study Bible.* Chattanooga: AMG Publishers, 1991. 1690.
55. Proverbs 14:12
56. Hebrews 12:2a
57. Matthew 22:39b
58. See I Kings 3:9.
59. Zodhiates, 1670.
60. Matthew 22:37
61. Matthew 22:39–40
62. Galatians 5:13–14
63. Proverbs 18:13
64. Matthew 23:11
65. Matthew 20:24
66. Matthew 20:26b–27
67. See Genesis 39–41.
68. Matthew 21:21
69. See Matthew 18:22.
70. Luke 17:5
71. See Luke 11:38.
72. Luke 17:1
73. Luke 17:6
74. See Mark 11:23.
75. Mark 11:25a
76. Matthew 6:15
77. Matthew 18:34–35
78. Matthew 18:10a
79. Psalm 127:3
80. Matthew 18:10b
81. Matthew 18:5
82. See Psalm 127:4–5.
83. Material taken from the notes of: Billica, Roger, Ph.D. "Achieving Health Without Treating Diseases." Lecture. Total Health Seminar. IBLP. ITC, Indianapolis. 3 Oct. 2007.
84. See I Kings 19:4–13.
85. See Jonah 4.
86. Psalm 103:2–3
87. I Thessalonians 5:18a
88. Proverbs 15:13
89. Isaiah 40:31
90. Galatians 6:9
91. Psalm 43:5
92. Proverbs 24:10
93. Hebrews 12:3
94. Hebrews 12:12–13

15. How Does Greed Affect the Immune System?

1. Our acquired immunity is divided into two lymphocyte-producing systems:

   A) Humoral immunity (B-cell), derived from cells in the fetal liver and bone. These go on to differentiate into immunoglobulins (IgA, IgM, IgG, IgE) also known as antibodies.

   B) Cell-mediated immunity (T-cell) derived from the fetal and infant thymus. These go on to differentiate into "helper" T cells, "cytotoxic" T cells, and "suppressor" T cells
2. Dhabhar, Firdaus S. "Acute Stress Enhances While Chronic Stress Suppresses Skin Immunity: The Role of Stress Hormones and Leukocyte Trafficking." *Annals of the New York Academy of Sciences* 917 (2000): 876–93.
3. Glaser, Ronald, Ph.D. and Janice K. Kiecolt-Glaser, Ph.D. "Stress-Associated Immune Modulation: Relevance to Viral Infections and Chronic Fatigue Syndrome." *American Journal of Medicine* 105 No. 3 Supplement 1 (1998): 35–42.
4. Black, P. H. "Immune System-Central Nervous System Interactions: Effect and Immunomodulatory Consequences of Immune System Mediators on the Brain." *Antimicrobial Agents and Chemotherapy* 38 No. 1 (1994): 7–12.
5. Fricchione, Gregory L. and George B. Stefano. "The Stress Response and Autoimmunoregulation." *Advances in Neuroimmunology* 4 No. 1 (1994): 13–27.
6. Invitti, C. "Obesity and Low-Grade Systemic Inflammation." *Minerva Endocrinologica* 27 No. 3 (2002): 209–14.
7. Devaraj, Sridevi and Ishwarlal Jialal. "Alpha Tocopherol Supplementation Decreases Serum C-Reactive Protein and Monocyte Interleukin-6 Levels in Normal Volunteers and Type 2 Diabetic Patients." *Free Radical Biology & Medicine* 29 No. 8 (2000): 790–92.
8. Dwyer, James H., Ph.D. "Arachidonate 5-Lipoxygenase Promoter Genotype, Dietary Arachidonic Acid, and Atherosclerosis." *New England Journal of Medicine* 350 No. 1 (2004): 29–37.
9. Schwarz, M. et al. "T-helper-1 and T-helper-2 Responses in Psychiatric Disorders." *Brain, Behavior, and Immunity* 15 (2001): 340–70.
10. Lucey, D. R., M. Clerici, and G. M. Shearer. "Type 1 and Type 2 Cytokine Dysregulation in Human Infectious, Neoplastic, and Inflammatory Diseases." *Clinical Microbiology Reviews* 9 No. 4 (1996): 532–62.

11. Subbaramaiah, K. et al. "Inhibition of Cyclooxygenase: A Novel Approach to Cancer Prevention." *Proc Soc Experimental Biology and Medicine* 216 (1997): 201–210.
12. I Timothy 6:9–10
13. Proverbs 28:22
14. Proverbs 15:27
15. Proverbs 23:5b
16. McLean, Bethany. "Valley of the Dollars." *Fortune* 14 Feb. 2006. 26 Apr. 2008 <http://money.cnn.com/magazines/fortune/fortune_archive/2006/02/20/8369114/index.htm>.
17. Saul, Stephanie. "Sleep Drugs Found Only Mildly Effective, but Wildly Popular." *New York Times* 23 Oct. 2007. 26 Apr. 2008 <http://www.nytimes.com/2007/10/23/health/23drug.html>.
18. Ecclesiastes 5:12
19. Irwin, M. et al. "Partial Night Sleep Deprivation Reduces Natural Killer and Cellular Immune Responses in Humans." *The FASEB Journal* 10 No. 5 (1996): 643–53.
20. Lange, Tanja, M.D. et al. "Shift of Monocyte Function Toward Cellular Immunity During Sleep." *Archives of Internal Medicine* 166 No. 16 (2006): 1695–1700.
21. Matthew 6:22–23
22. In much the same way that fire consumes material and leaves ashes, rust oxidizes metal and leaves "ashes" behind.
23. James 5:3–4
24. Matthew 6:23a
25. Barlett, Donald L. and James B. Steele. *Howard Hughes: His Life and Madness.* New York: W.W. Norton & Company, Inc., 2004.
26. Proverbs 22:4
27. Deuteronomy 8:18b
28. I Timothy 6:8
29. II Corinthians 9:10
30. Psalm 112:1b, 3, 9a
31. Matthew 5:16a
32. Ephesians 2:10
33. Titus 2:14
34. Hebrews 10:24b
35. Titus 3:1b
36. Matthew 5:14a
37. Matthew 5:16b
38. Luke 4:18–19
39. John 14:12
40. See Luke 24:49 and John 16:7–8.
41. II Timothy 1:6b
42. Ibid.
43. Matthew 6:20
44. Malachi 3:10
45. Proverbs 3:9–10b
46. See Galatians 3.
47. II Corinthians 9:6
48. II Corinthians 9:8
49. II Corinthians 9:10b
50. II Corinthians 9:11
51. Luke 6:38a
52. See Deuteronomy 14:23.
53. Matthew 6:33
54. Ephesians 5:5b
55. Matthew 6:24
56. See Hebrews 1:3.
57. John 15:7–8
58. See I Corinthians 9:11.
59. See Matthew 6:33.
60. See Matthew 6:25–30.
61. Luke 12:15a
62. Exodus 20:17
63. Luke 12:15b
64. Luke 12:21
65. Psalm 37:4
66. I Corinthians 12:31a
67. See I Corinthians 14:39.
68. Jeremiah 45:5
69. Luke 14:13
70. Matthew 6:21
71. Acts 20:35b
72. Luke 14:14
73. Matthew 25:40b
74. Matthew 7:7
75. Matthew 6:11
76. Philippians 4:19
77. James 4:2b
78. James 4:3
79. See Exodus 2–13.
80. Matthew 22:21
81. Romans 13:4–7
82. I Timothy 2:2b–4
83. Romans 13:4a
84. Gothard, Bill. IBLP Newsletter July 1998. IBLP, 1998. 2.

16. How Does Fear Affect the Respiratory System?

1. Psalm 112:7–8a
2. John 8:32
3. Deuteronomy 20:8
4. Rosenthal, R. R. et al. "Role of the Parasympathetic System in Antigen-Induced Bronchospasm." *Journal of Applied Physiology* 42 No. 4 (1977): 600–06.
5. Gerlach, Alexander L., Frank H. Wilhelm, and Walton T. Roth. "Embarrassment and Social Phobia: the Role of Parasympathetic Activation." *Journal of Anxiety Disorders* 17 No. 2 (2003): 197–210.
6. Robert, Caroline, M.D. and Thomas S. Kupper M.D. "Mechanisms of Disease: Inflammatory Skin Diseases, T Cells, and Immune Surveillance." *New England Journal of Medicine* 341 No. 24 (1999): 1817–28.
7. Joachim, R. A. et al. "Neuronal Plasticity of the 'Brain-Skin Connection': Stress-Triggered Up-Regulation of Neuropeptides in Dorsal Root Ganglia and Skin via Nerve Growth Factor-Dependent Pathways." *Journal of Molecular Medicine* 85 No. 12 (2007): 1347–49.
8. Karsarou-Katsari, Alexandra, Leena K Singh, and Theoharis C. Theoharides. "Alopecia areata and Affected Skin CRH Receptor Up-Regulation Induced by Acute Emotional Stress." *Dermatology* 203 No. 2 (2001): 157–61.
9. Paus, Ralf, Theoharis C. Theoharides, and Petra Clara Arck. "Neuroimmunoendocrine Circuitry of the 'Brain-Skin Connection.' " *Trends in Immunology* 27 No. 1 (2006): 32–39.
10. Laederach-Hofmann, Kurt M.D., F.M.H, A.P.P.M. et al. "Patients With Erythrophobia (Fear of Blushing) Show Abnormal Autonomic Regulation in Mental Stress Conditions." *Psychosomatic Medicine* 64 No. 2 (2002): 358–65.
11. Sandburg, Seija et al. "The Role of Acute and Chronic Stress in Asthma Attacks in Children." *The Lancet* 356 No. 9234 (2000): 982–87.
12. Dawson, Deborah A. "Family Structure and Children's Health and Well-Being: Data from the 1988 National Health Interview Survey on Child Health." *Journal of Marriage and the Family* 53 No. 3 (1991): 573–84.
13. Roitt, Ivan, Jonathan Brostoff, and David Male. *Immunology* 5th ed. N.p.: Mosby-Year Book, 1998.
14. Farrerons-Co, J. et al. "Cell-Mediated Immune Reactions in Asthma." *Clinical & Experimental Allergy* 8 No. 5 (1978): 463–69.
15. See Romans 8:28 and Hebrews 13:5.
16. See Psalm 1:3.
17. Matthew 16:25
18. Matthew 4:19
19. Psalm 23:4
20. James 1:14–15
21. Judges 6:12
22. Genesis 28:14b
23. Matthew 28:19–20
24. Matthew 11:29–30
25. Bowen, Barbara MacDonald. *Strange Scriptures That Perplex the Western Mind.* Palestine: Wm. B. Eerdmans, 1940. 43.
26. "Who will you follow?" Article III. *Resources Page.* Online Bible School. 18 Feb. 2008 <http://theonlinebibleschool.net/mod/resource/view.php?id=190>.
27. See Matthew 15:3–9 and Mark 7:6–13.
28. Matthew 11:28–30
29. Romans 7:10
30. I John 5:3
31. See John 1:29.
32. Matthew 10:16
33. Proverbs 13:20
34. I Corinthians 1:26–27, 29
35. Revelation 12:11
36. I Peter 5:8
37. Mark 11:17b
38. II Timothy 1:7
39. I Corinthians 6:19
40. See Romans 12:1–2.
41. See Luke 19:46.
42. Romans 12:2
43. Jeremiah 33:3
44. Psalm 50:15
45. See Mark 12:30.
46. Luke 24:49b
47. I John 4:18
48. See Romans 8:9, 10:9.
49. See I Thessalonians 5:23.
50. Luke 11:11, 13
51. Ephesians 5:18
52. See Luke 4:1–14.
53. See I Peter 1:23.
54. See II Peter 3:18.
55. See Romans 5:3–5.
56. Matthew 26:41a
57. See I Peter 5:8–9.
58. See Revelation 3:14–22.
59. Matthew 6:13a
60. Hebrews 3:13
61. Matthew 10:28a
62. Hebrews 2:14b–15
63. Lubitz, James D. and Gerald F. Riley. "Trends in Medicare Payments in the Last Year of Life." *New England Journal of Medicine* 328 No. 15 (1993): 1092–96.

64. Hogan, Christopher et al. "Medicare Beneficiaries' Costs Of Care In The Last Year Of Life." *Health Affairs* 20 No. 4 (2001): 188–95.
65. Calfo, Steve, Jonathan Smith, and Mark Zezza. "Last Year of Life." *CMS Page.* USDHHS. 14 Dec. 2005. 28 Apr. 2008 <http://www.cms.hhs.gov/ActuarialStudies/ 03_Last_Year_of_Life.asp>.
66. Tson, Josef, *Three Secrets for Conquering Fear.* DVD. Institute in Basic Life Principles, 2005.
67. I Thessalonians 4:13
68. See Ephesians 2:10.
69. See Colossians 1:28–29.
70. See Philippians 1:21–24.
71. Tyerman, Luke. *The Life and Times of the Rev. John Wesley, M.A., Founder of the Methodists.* New York: Harper & Bros., 1872. 632.
72. Tson.

17. How Does Envy Affect the Musculoskeletal System?

1. Guyton, Arthur C. and John E. Hall. *Textbook of Medical Physiology.* 11th ed. Philadelphia: W. B. Saunders Co., 2005. 929.
2. In mature cortical (outer calcified layer) bone, there are three cell types that are responsible for production and maintenance:
   Osteoblasts. These produce collagen (a flexible fiber), which makes up 90% of the bone and gives it powerful strength. They are actively working throughout life but are influenced by stress and growth hormones.
   Osteocytes. These are the most abundant cells found in bone. Once osteoblasts become trapped in the matrix they secrete, they become osteocytes.
   Osteoclasts. These produce enzymes that dissolve calcified bone and make it available for reconstruction.
3. Bushinsky, David A. et al. "Chronic Acidosis-Induced Alteration in Bone Bicarbonate Phosphate." *American Journal of Physiology-Renal Physiology* 285 (2003): 532–39.
4. Osteoporosis Progress and Promise: NIAMS." *Articles Page.* WD. n.d. 28 Apr. 2008 <http://www.wrongdiagnosis.com/artic/osteoporosis_progress_and_promise_niams.htm >.
5. See Proverbs 14:30.
6. Proverbs 27:4
7. See Acts 7:9.
8. See Mark 15:10.
9. Pansky, Ben. *Review of Gross Anatomy* 4th ed. New York: MacMillan, 1979. 235, 453.
10. Symptoms of Hormone Disturbance." *Cancer Symptoms Page.* ONS. n.d. 28 Apr. 2008 <http://www.cancersymptoms.org/hormonal/symptoms.shtml>.
11. Rice, M. Katherine. Ed. *Taber's Cyclopedic Medical Dictionary* 14th ed. Philadelphia: F. A. Davis Co., 1983. 1010.
12. Psalm 31:10
13. Proverbs 14:30
14. "Cortisol Levels, Thyroid Function and Aging." *Virginia Hopkins Health Watch Page.* One to One Inc. n.d. 28 Apr. 2008 <http://www.virginiahopkinstestkits.com/cortisolzava.html>.
15. Jackson, Rebecca D., M.D. et al. "Calcium Plus Vitamin D Supplementation and the Risk of Fractures." *New England Journal of Medicine* 354 No. 7 (2006): 669–83.
16. Wyngaarden, James B., Lloyd H. Smith, and J. Claude Bennett. *Cecil Textbook of Medicine* 19th ed. Philadelphia: W. B. Saunders Co., 1991. 1412–15.
17. See Leviticus 17:14.
18. Proverbs 3:7–8
19. See Acts 7:9.
20. Proverbs 23:17–18
21. Matthew 20:27
22. Philippians 2:20–21
23. Romans 12:10
24. See Exodus 4:1–5; 7:10, 19–20.
25. Matthew 7:12a
26. Matthew 7:12b
27. See Esther 8.
28. John 14:15
29. See Matthew 5:21–30.
30. John 1:17
31. Deuteronomy 5:1b
32. See John 21:16.
33. Ezekiel 34:4a
34. Matthew 10:1b
35. Luke 24:32
36. Luke 24:27
37. John 10:11b
38. Matthew 28:19
39. See Acts 10:47.
40. See Matthew 3:11.
41. I Peter 3:21
42. Acts 2:1, 3–4
43. Acts 8:18. See also Acts 19:6.
44. See Acts 9:17.
45. II Timothy 1:6b
46. See Numbers 31:21–24.
47. Hebrews 6:1–2
48. Matthew 28:19–20
49. John 17:21
50. See Matthew 28:20.
51. John 15:14–15
52. John 15:7–8
53. II Timothy 2:2
54. Acts 14:22b
55. Matthew 7:6a
56. Acts 8:9b
57. Acts 8:18–19
58. Acts 8:20–21, 23
59. Proverbs 23:9
60. Proverbs 9:7–8a
61. Mathew 9:38
62. See John 16:23.
63. See Matthew 10:16.
64. See Acts 13:2.
65. Matthew 10:1b
66. John 4:35

18. The Secret to Renewing Your Strength

1. Isaiah 40:29–31
2. James 1:8
3. Psalm 62:5
4. Isaiah 40:31
5. I Corinthians 15:10b
6. Matthew 11:28–30
7. Psalm 27:14
8. Psalm 130:5–6